Ernest Hemingway

The Old Man and the Sea

Herausgegeben von
Hans-Christian Oeser

Philipp Reclam jun. Stuttgart

To Charles Scribner
and to Max Perkins

RECLAMS UNIVERSAL-BIBLIOTHEK Nr. 9075
Alle Rechte vorbehalten
Copyright für diese Ausgabe
© 2000 Philipp Reclam jun. GmbH & Co. KG, Stuttgart
Copyright für den Text © Hemingway Foreign Rights Trust. Reprinted by permission of The Hemingway Foreign Rights Trust, Bozeman (Montana)
Umschlagabbildung: Szenenfoto aus dem Fernsehfilm (USA 1988, Regie: Judd Taylor) mit Anthony Quinn (Filmdokumentationszentrum Wien)
Gesamtherstellung: Reclam, Ditzingen. Printed in Germany 2010
RECLAM, UNIVERSAL-BIBLIOTHEK und RECLAMS
UNIVERSAL-BIBLIOTHEK sind eingetragene Marken
der Philipp Reclam jun. GmbH & Co. KG, Stuttgart
ISBN 978-3-15-009075-6

www.reclam.de

The Old Man and the Sea

He was an old man who fished alone in a skiff in the
Gulf Stream and he had gone eighty-four days now
without taking a fish. In the first forty days a boy had
5 been with him. But after forty days without a fish the
boy's parents had told him that the old man was now
definitely and finally *salao*, which is the worst form of
unlucky, and the boy had gone at their orders in another boat which caught three good fish the first week.
10 It made the boy sad to see the old man come in each
day with his skiff empty and he always went down to
help him carry either the coiled lines or the gaff and
harpoon and the sail that was furled around the mast.
The sail was patched with flour sacks and, furled, it
15 looked like the flag of permanent defeat.

The old man was thin and gaunt with deep wrinkles
in the back of his neck. The brown blotches of the be-

---

2 **skiff:** Skiff (kleines, leichtes Ruderboot mit Segel).
3 **Gulf Stream:** Golfstrom.
7 **salao** (Span., coll.): vom Pech verfolgt.
12 **to coil:** aufrollen, -schießen, in Ringen übereinander legen.
   gaff: Fisch-, Landungshaken.
13 **harpoon:** Harpune.
   to furl: rollen, schlagen, wickeln.
16 **gaunt:** hager, ausgezehrt.
   wrinkle: Falte, Furche, Runzel.
17 **blotch:** Fleck.
17f. **benevolent:** gutartig, harmlos.

nevolent skin cancer the sun brings from its reflection
on the tropic sea were on his cheeks. The blotches ran
well down the sides of his face and his hands had the
deep-creased scars from handling heavy fish on the
5 cords. But none of these scars were fresh. They were as
old as erosions in a fishless desert.

Everything about him was old except his eyes and
they were the same colour as the sea and were cheerful
and undefeated.

10 "Santiago," the boy said to him as they climbed the
bank from where the skiff was hauled up. "I could go
with you again. We've made some money."

The old man had taught the boy to fish and the boy
loved him.

15 "No," the old man said. "You're with a lucky boat.
Stay with them."

"But remember how you went eighty-seven days
without fish and then we caught big ones every day for
three weeks."

20 "I remember," the old man said. "I know you did not
leave me because you doubted."

"It was papa made me leave. I am a boy and I must
obey him."

"I know," the old man said. "It is quite normal."

25 "He hasn't much faith."

"No," the old man said. "But we have. Haven't we?"

---

4 **deep-creased:** tief eingekerbt.
6 **erosion:** Erosion, Abtragung, Auswaschung, -höhlung.
10 **Santiago** (Span.): meist in geographischen Namen verwendete Zu-
sammenziehung von *San Diego*, St. Jakobus dem Älteren (Fischer
und Jünger Jesu; spanischer Nationalheiliger).
22 **papa made me leave:** *papa who made me leave.*

"Yes," the boy said. "Can I offer you a beer on the Terrace and then we'll take the stuff home."

"Why not?" the old man said. "Between fishermen."

They sat on the Terrace and many of the fishermen
5 made fun of the old man and he was not angry. Others, of the older fishermen, looked at him and were sad. But they did not show it and they spoke politely about the current and the depths they had drifted their lines at and the steady good weather and of what they had
10 seen. The successful fishermen of that day were already in and had butchered their marlin out and carried them laid full length across two planks, with two men staggering at the end of each plank, to the fish house where they waited for the ice truck to carry them to the mar-
15 ket in Havana. Those who had caught sharks had taken them to the shark factory on the other side of the cove where they were hoisted on a block and tackle, their livers removed, their fins cut off and their hides skinned out and their flesh cut into strips for salting.
20 When the wind was in the east a smell came across the harbour from the shark factory; but today there

---

2 **Terrace:** Name eines Lokals (von span. *terraza* ›Straßencafé‹).
3 **fisherman:** Fischer.
8 **to drift:** treiben lassen.
11 **to butcher out:** ausschlachten, -nehmen, -weiden.
 marlin (pl. *marlin*): Marlin (Gattung der Fächerfische mit schwertartig ausgezogenem Oberkiefer).
12 **plank:** Planke, Bohle.
12f. **to stagger:** taumeln, torkeln, schwanken, wanken.
13 **fish house:** Fischhalle.
16 **cove:** (kleine) Bucht.
17 **to hoist:** hochheben, -winden, -ziehen.
 block and tackle: Flaschenzug.
18 **fin:** Finne, Flosse.

was only the faint edge of the odour because the wind
had backed into the north and then dropped off and it
was pleasant and sunny on the Terrace.

"Santiago," the boy said.

5   "Yes," the old man said. He was holding his glass and
thinking of many years ago.

"Can I go out and get sardines for you for tomorrow?"

"No. Go and play baseball. I can still row and Roge-
10 lio will throw the net."

"I would like to go. If I cannot fish with you, I would
like to serve in some way."

"You bought me a beer," the old man said. "You are
already a man."

15   "How old was I when you first took me in a boat?"

"Five and you nearly were killed when I brought the
fish in too green and he nearly tore the boat to pieces.
Can you remember?"

"I can remember the tail slapping and banging and
20 the thwart breaking and the noise of the clubbing. I can
remember you throwing me into the bow where the
wet coiled lines were and feeling the whole boat shiver
and the noise of you clubbing him like chopping a tree
down and the sweet blood smell all over me."

25   "Can you really remember that or did I just tell it to
you?"

---

    1 **odour:** Geruch.
    2 **to back:** drehen (Wind).
   17 **green:** hier: frisch.
   19 **to slap:** klatschen, schlagen.
       to bang: knallen, krachen.
   20 **thwart:** Ducht, Ruderbank.
   22 **to shiver:** beben.

6

"I remember everything from when we first went together."

The old man looked at him with his sun-burned, confident, loving eyes.

"If you were my boy I'd take you out and gamble," he said. "But you are your father's and your mother's and you are in a lucky boat."

"May I get the sardines? I know where I can get four baits too."

"I have mine left from today. I put them in salt in the box."

"Let me get four fresh ones."

"One," the old man said. His hope and his confidence had never gone. But now they were freshening as when the breeze rises.

"Two," the boy said.

"Two," the old man agreed. "You didn't steal them?"

"I would," the boy said. "But I bought these."

"Thank you," the old man said. He was too simple to wonder when he had attained humility. But he knew he had attained it and he knew it was not disgraceful and it carried no loss of true pride.

"Tomorrow is going to be a good day with this current," he said.

"Where are you going?" the boy asked.

---

3 **sun-burned:** sonnenverbrannt.
5 **to gamble:** sein Glück versuchen, es riskieren.
9 **bait:** Köder.
14 **to freshen:** aufleben, sich beleben.
15 **breeze:** Brise, (leichter) Wind.
20 **to attain:** erlangen.
   humility: Bescheidenheit, Demut.
21 **disgraceful:** schändlich, schimpflich.

"Far out to come in when the wind shifts. I want to be out before it is light."

"I'll try to get him to work far out," the boy said. "Then if you hook something truly big we can come to your aid."

"He does not like to work too far out."

"No," the boy said. "But I will see something that he cannot see such as a bird working and get him to come out after dolphin."

"Are his eyes that bad?"

"He is almost blind."

"It is strange," the old man said. "He never went turtle-ing. That is what kills the eyes."

"But you went turtle-ing for years off the Mosquito Coast and your eyes are good."

"I am a strange old man."

"But are you strong enough now for a truly big fish?"

"I think so. And there are many tricks."

"Let us take the stuff home," the boy said. "So I can get the cast net and go after the sardines."

They picked up the gear from the boat. The old man carried the mast on his shoulder and the boy carried the wooden box with the coiled, hard-braided brown lines, the gaff and the harpoon with its shaft. The box

---

3 **to work:** hier: rudern.
4 **to hook:** an die Angel bekommen, fangen.
8 **to work:** hier: Futter, Nahrung suchen.
9 **dolphin:** Delphinfisch(e), Goldmakrele(n).
13 **to turtle:** auf Schildkrötenfang fahren.
14 f. **Mosquito Coast:** *Costa de Mosquitos*, Moskitoküste (Ostküste Nicaraguas).
20 **cast net:** Wurfnetz.
23 **hard-braided:** fest geflochten.
24 **shaft:** Schaft.

with the baits was under the stern of the skiff along with the club that was used to subdue the big fish when they were brought alongside. No one would steal from the old man but it was better to take the sail and
5 the heavy lines home as the dew was bad for them and, though he was quite sure no local people would steal from him, the old man thought that a gaff and a harpoon were needless temptations to leave in a boat.
10 They walked up the road together to the old man's shack and went in through its open door. The old man leaned the mast with its wrapped sail against the wall and the boy put the box and the other gear beside it. The mast was nearly as long as the one room of the
15 shack. The shack was made of the tough bud-shields of the royal palm which are called *guano* and in it there was a bed, a table, one chair, and a place on the dirt floor to cook with charcoal. On the brown walls of the flattened, overlapping leaves of the sturdy-fibred
20 *guano* there was a picture in colour of the Sacred Heart

---

1 **stern:** Heck.
2 **to subdue:** bändigen, bezwingen.
3 **alongside** (adv.): längsseits.
5 **dew:** Tau.
8 **needless:** überflüssig, unnötig.
11 **shack:** Hütte.
15 **bud-shield:** Knospenhülle.
16 **royal palm:** Königspalme (Palmenart auf Kuba).
　　guano (Am. Span.): Palme; Palmwedel.
18 **charcoal:** Holzkohle.
19 **to flatten:** glatt machen, platt drücken.
　　to overlap: überlappen, (teilweise) übereinander liegen.
　　sturdy-fibred: hartfaserig.
20 f. **Sacred Heart of Jesus:** Heiliges Herz Jesu.

of Jesus and another of the Virgin of Cobre. These were relics of his wife. Once there had been a tinted photograph of his wife on the wall but he had taken it down because it made him too lonely to see it and it was on the shelf in the corner under his clean shirt.

"What do you have to eat?" the boy asked.

"A pot of yellow rice with fish. Do you want some?"

"No. I will eat at home. Do you want me to make the fire?"

"No. I will make it later on. Or I may eat the rice cold."

"May I take the cast net?"

"Of course."

There was no cast net and the boy remembered when they had sold it. But they went through this fiction every day. There was no pot of yellow rice and fish and the boy knew this too.

"Eighty-five is a lucky number," the old man said. "How would you like to see me bring one in that dressed out over a thousand pounds?"

"I'll get the cast net and go for sardines. Will you sit in the sun in the doorway?"

"Yes. I have yesterday's paper and I will read the baseball."

The boy did not know whether yesterday's paper was a fiction too. But the old man brought it out from under the bed.

---

1 **Virgin of Cobre:** Jungfrau von Cobre; gemeint ist die Schutzheilige Kubas, La Virgen de la Caridad del Cobre (*El Cobre:* Stadt im Südosten Kubas bei Santiago de Cuba).
2 **relic:** Relikt; Reliquie.
  to tint: kolorieren, tönen.
20 **to dress out:** etwa: in ausgenommenem Zustand wiegen.

"Perico gave it to me at the *bodega*," he explained.

"I'll be back when I have the sardines. I'll keep yours and mine together on ice and we can share them in the morning. When I come back you can tell me about the baseball."

"The Yankees cannot lose."

"But I fear the Indians of Cleveland."

"Have faith in the Yankees my son. Think of the great DiMaggio."

"I fear both the Tigers of Detroit and the Indians of Cleveland."

"Be careful or you will fear even the Reds of Cincinnati and the White Sox of Chicago."

"You study it and tell me when I come back."

"Do you think we should buy a terminal of the lottery with an eighty-five? Tomorrow is the eighty-fifth day."

"We can do that," the boy said. "But what about the eighty-seven of your great record?"

"It could not happen twice. Do you think you can find an eighty-five?"

"I can order one."

"One sheet. That's two dollars and a half. Who can we borrow that from?"

"That's easy. I can always borrow two dollars and a half."

---

1 **bodega** (Span.): Weinkeller, -lokal; Lebensmittelgeschäft.

6 ff. **Yankees / Indians of Cleveland / Tigers of Detroit / Reds of Cincinnati / White Sox of Chicago:** *New York Yankees, Cleveland Indians, Detroit Tigers, Cincinnati Reds, Chicago White Sox:* bekannte amerikanische Baseballmannschaften.

15 **terminal:** Los für die letzte Ziehung.

15 f. **lottery:** Lotterie.

"I think perhaps I can too. But I try not to borrow. First you borrow. Then you beg."

"Keep warm old man," the boy said. "Remember we are in September."

5 "The month when the great fish come," the old man said. "Anyone can be a fisherman in May."

"I go now for the sardines," the boy said.

When the boy came back the old man was asleep in the chair and the sun was down. The boy took the old 10 army blanket off the bed and spread it over the back of the chair and over the old man's shoulders. They were strange shoulders, still powerful although very old, and the neck was still strong too and the creases did not show so much when the old man was asleep and his 15 head fallen forward. His shirt had been patched so many times that it was like the sail and the patches were faded to many different shades by the sun. The old man's head was very old though and with his eyes closed there was no life in his face. The newspaper lay 20 across his knees and the weight of his arm held it there in the evening breeze. He was barefooted.

The boy left him there and when he came back the old man was still asleep.

"Wake up old man," the boy said and put his hand 25 on one of the old man's knees.

The old man opened his eyes and for a moment he was coming back from a long way away. Then he smiled.

"What have you got?" he asked.

---

13 **crease:** Falte, Furche, Runzel.
21 **barefooted** (auch: *barefoot*): barfuß.

"Supper," said the boy. "We're going to have supper."

"I'm not very hungry."

"Come on and eat. You can't fish and not eat."

5 "I have," the old man said getting up and taking the newspaper and folding it. Then he started to fold the blanket.

"Keep the blanket around you," the boy said. "You'll not fish without eating while I'm alive."

10 "Then live a long time and take care of yourself," the old man said. "What are we eating?"

"Black beans and rice, fried bananas, and some stew."

The boy had brought them in a two-decker metal
15 container from the Terrace. The two sets of knives and forks and spoons were in his pocket with a paper napkin wrapped around each set.

"Who gave this to you?"

"Martin. The owner."

20 "I must thank him."

"I thanked him already," the boy said. "You don't need to thank him."

"I'll give him the belly meat of a big fish," the old man said. "Has he done this for us more than once?"

25 "I think so."

"I must give him something more than the belly meat then. He is very thoughtful for us."

"He sent two beers."

---

13 **stew:** Eintopf.
14 **two-decker:** zweistöckig.
16 f. **napkin:** Serviette.
27 **thoughtful:** aufmerksam, hilfsbereit.

"I like the beer in cans best."

"I know. But this is in bottles, Hatuey beer, and I take back the bottles."

"That's very kind of you," the old man said. "Should we eat?"

"I've been asking you to," the boy told him gently. "I have not wished to open the container until you were ready."

"I'm ready now," the old man said. "I only needed time to wash."

Where did you wash? the boy thought. The village water supply was two streets down the road. I must have water here for him, the boy thought, and soap and a good towel. Why am I so thoughtless? I must get him another shirt and a jacket for the winter and some sort of shoes and another blanket.

"Your stew is excellent," the old man said.

"Tell me about the baseball," the boy asked him.

"In the American League it is the Yankees as I said," the old man said happily.

"They lost today," the boy told him.

"That means nothing. The great DiMaggio is himself again."

"They have other men on the team."

"Naturally. But he makes the difference. In the other league, between Brooklyn and Philadelphia I must take Brooklyn. But then I think of Dick Sisler and those great drives in the old park."

"There was nothing ever like them. He hits the longest ball I have ever seen."

---

19 **American League:** Amerikanische (Baseball-)Liga.
28 **drive:** Treibschlag, weiter Schlag (Sport).

14

"Do you remember when he used to come to the Terrace? I wanted to take him fishing but I was too timid to ask him. Then I asked you to ask him and you were too timid."

5 "I know. It was a great mistake. He might have gone with us. Then we would have that for all of our lives."

"I would like to take the great DiMaggio fishing," the old man said. "They say his father was a fisherman. Maybe he was as poor as we are and would under-
10 stand."

"The great Sisler's father was never poor and he, the father, was playing in the big leagues when he was my age."

"When I was your age I was before the mast on a
15 square-rigged ship that ran to Africa and I have seen lions on the beaches in the evening."

"I know. You told me."

"Should we talk about Africa or about baseball?"

"Baseball I think," the boy said. "Tell me about the
20 great John J. McGraw." He said *Jota* for J.

"He used to come to the Terrace sometimes too in the older days. But he was rough and harsh-spoken and difficult when he was drinking. His mind was on horses as well as baseball. At least he carried lists of horses at
25 all times in his pocket and frequently spoke the names of horses on the telephone."

"He was a great manager," the boy said. "My father thinks he was the greatest."

"Because he came here the most times," the old man

15 **square-rigged:** vollgetakelt (*to rig:* auftakeln).
20 **Jota:** griechischer Buchstabe.
22 **harsh-spoken:** barsch, schroff.

said. "If Durocher had continued to come here each year your father would think him the greatest manager."

"Who is the greatest manager, really, Luque or Mike Gonzalez?"

"I think they are equal."

"And the best fisherman is you."

"No. I know others better."

"Qué va," the boy said. "There are many good fishermen and some great ones. But there is only you."

"Thank you. You make me happy. I hope no fish will come along so great that he will prove us wrong."

"There is no such fish if you are still strong as you say."

"I may not be as strong as I think," the old man said. "But I know many tricks and I have resolution."

"You ought to go to bed now so that you will be fresh in the morning. I will take the things back to the Terrace."

"Good night then. I will wake you in the morning."

"You're my alarm clock," the boy said.

"Age is my alarm clock," the old man said. "Why do old men wake so early? Is it to have one longer day?"

"I don't know," the boy said. "All I know is that young boys sleep late and hard."

"I can remember it," the old man said. "I'll waken you in time."

"I do not like for him to waken me. It is as though I were inferior."

---

9 **qué va** (Span.): auf keinen Fall, nicht doch.
25 **to sleep hard:** fest, tief schlafen.
26 **to waken:** (auf)wecken.

"I know."

"Sleep well old man."

The boy went out. They had eaten with no light on the table and the old man took off his trousers and went to bed in the dark. He rolled his trousers up to make a pillow, putting the newspaper inside them. He rolled himself in the blanket and slept on the other old newspapers that covered the springs of the bed.

He was asleep in a short time and he dreamed of Africa when he was a boy and the long, golden beaches and the white beaches, so white they hurt your eyes, and the high capes and the great brown mountains. He lived along that coast now every night and in his dreams he heard the surf roar and saw the native boats come riding through it. He smelled the tar and oakum of the deck as he slept and he smelled the smell of Africa that the land breeze brought at morning.

Usually when he smelled the land breeze he woke up and dressed to go and wake the boy. But tonight the smell of the land breeze came very early and he knew it was too early in his dream and went on dreaming to see the white peaks of the Islands rising from the sea and then he dreamed of the different harbours and roadsteads of the Canary Islands.

He no longer dreamed of storms, nor of women, nor

---

13 **cape:** Kap (vorspringender Teil einer Felsenküste).
15 **surf:** Brandung.
16 **tar:** Teer.
   oakum: Werg (Hanffasern).
25 **roadstead:** Reede, Ankerplatz.
   Canary Islands: Kanarische Inseln.

of great occurrences, nor of great fish, nor fights, nor contests of strength, nor of his wife. He only dreamed of places now and of the lions on the beach. They played like young cats in the dusk and he loved them as he loved the boy. He never dreamed about the boy. He simply woke, looked out the open door at the moon and unrolled his trousers and put them on. He urinated outside the shack and then went up the road to wake the boy. He was shivering with the morning cold. But he knew he would shiver himself warm and that soon he would be rowing.

The door of the house where the boy lived was unlocked and he opened it and walked in quietly with his bare feet. The boy was asleep on a cot in the first room and the old man could see him clearly with the light that came in from the dying moon. He took hold of one foot gently and held it until the boy woke and turned and looked at him. The old man nodded and the boy took his trousers from the chair by the bed and, sitting on the bed, pulled them on.

The old man went out the door and the boy came after him. He was sleepy and the old man put his arm across his shoulders and said, "I am sorry."

"Qué va," the boy said. "It is what a man must do."

They walked down the road to the old man's shack and all along the road, in the dark, barefoot men were moving, carrying the masts of their boats.

---

2 **contest of strength:** Kräftemessen, Kraftprobe.
4 **dusk:** Abenddämmerung, Einbruch der Dunkelheit.
7 **to urinate:** urinieren, Wasser lassen.
9 **to shiver:** erschauern, frösteln, zittern.
14 **cot:** Bett-, Schlafstelle; Lager.

When they reached the old man's shack the boy took the rolls of line in the basket and the harpoon and gaff and the old man carried the mast with the furled sail on his shoulder.

5 "Do you want coffee?" the boy asked.

"We'll put the gear in the boat and then get some."

They had coffee from condensed-milk cans at an early morning place that served fishermen.

"How did you sleep old man?" the boy asked. He 10 was waking up now although it was still hard for him to leave his sleep.

"Very well, Manolin," the old man said. "I feel confident today."

"So do I," the boy said. "Now I must get your sar- 15 dines and mine and your fresh baits. He brings our gear himself. He never wants anyone to carry anything."

"We're different," the old man said. "I let you carry things when you were five years old."

"I know it," the boy said. "I'll be right back. Have 20 another coffee. We have credit here."

He walked off, barefooted on the coral rocks, to the ice house where the baits were stored.

The old man drank his coffee slowly. It was all he would have all day and he knew that he should take it. 25 For a long time now eating had bored him and he never carried a lunch. He had a bottle of water in the bow of the skiff and that was all he needed for the day.

The boy was back now with the sardines and the two baits wrapped in a newspaper and they went down the

---

7 **condensed-milk:** Kondensmilch.
8 **place:** Lokal.
21 **coral rock:** Korallenfels.

trail to the skiff, feeling the pebbled sand unter their feet, and lifted the skiff and slid her into the water.

"Good luck old man."

"Good luck," the old man said. He fitted the rope
5 lashings of the oars onto the thole pins and, leaning forward against the thrust of the blades in the water, he began to row out of the harbour in the dark. There were other boats from the other beaches going out to sea and the old man heard the dip and push of their
10 oars even though he could not see them now the moon was below the hills.

Sometimes someone would speak in a boat. But most of the boats were silent except for the dip of the oars. They spread apart after they were out of the mouth of
15 the harbour and each one headed for the part of the ocean where he hoped to find fish. The old man knew he was going far out and he left the smell of the land behind and rowed out into the clean early morning smell of the ocean. He saw the phosphorescence of
20 the Gulf weed in the water as he rowed over the part of the ocean that the fishermen called the great well because there was a sudden deep of seven hundred

---

1 **trail:** Pfad, Weg.
  pebbled: kieselig, steinig.
4 f. **rope lashing:** Tauwerk, Zurring (Leine, Seil zum Zurren).
5 **oar:** Riemen, Ruder.
  thole pin: Dolle.
6 **thrust:** Druck.
9 **dip:** Eintauchen.
14 **to spread apart:** sich ausbreiten, verteilen.
19 **phosphorescence:** Phosphoreszenz, Phosphorisieren, Leuchten.
20 **weed:** Seetang, Meeresalgen.
22 **deep:** Tiefe.

fathoms where all sorts of fish congregated because of the swirl the current made against the steep walls of the floor of the ocean. Here there were concentrations of shrimp and bait fish and sometimes schools of
5 squid in the deepest holes and these rose close to the surface at night where all the wandering fish fed on them.

In the dark the old man could feel the morning coming and as he rowed he heard the trembling sound as
10 flying fish left the water and the hissing that their stiff set wings made as they soared away in the darkness. He was very fond of flying fish as they were his principal friends on the ocean. He was sorry for the birds, especially the small delicate dark terns that were always fly-
15 ing and looking and almost never finding, and he thought, "The birds have a harder life than we do except for the robber birds and the heavy strong ones. Why did they make birds so delicate and fine as those sea swallows when the ocean can be so cruel? She is
20 kind and very beautiful. But she can be so cruel and it comes so suddenly and such birds that fly, dipping and hunting, with their small sad voices are made too delicately for the sea."

1 **fathom:** Faden (Maßeinheit zur Angabe der Wassertiefe; entspricht etwa 1,80 m).
2 **swirl:** Wirbel.
4 **shrimp:** Garnele.
  school: Schwarm.
5 **squid:** Tintenfisch.
10 **to hiss:** zische(l)n.
11 **to soar:** aufsteigen, segeln, schweben.
14 **tern:** Meer-, Seeschwalbe.
17 **robber bird:** Raubvogel.
21 **to dip:** hinunterstoßen.

He always thought of the sea as *la mar* which is what people call her in Spanish when they love her. Sometimes those who love her say bad things of her but they are always said as though she were a woman. Some of
5 the younger fishermen, those who used buoys as floats for their lines and had motor-boats, bought when the shark livers had brought much money, spoke of her as *el mar* which is masculine. They spoke of her as a contestant or a place or even an enemy. But the old man
10 always thought of her as feminine and as something that gave or withheld great favours, and if she did wild or wicked things it was because she could not help them. The moon affects her as it does a woman, he thougt.

15 He was rowing steadily and it was no effort for him since he kept well within his speed and the surface of the ocean was flat except for the occasional swirls of the current. He was letting the current do a third of the work and as it started to be light he saw he was already
20 further out than he had hoped to be at this hour.

I worked the deep wells for a week and did nothing, he thought. Today I'll work out where the schools of bonita and albacore are and maybe there will be a big one with them.

25 Before it was really light he had his baits out and was

---

5 **buoy:** Boje.
   float: Schwimmer (Fischfang).
8 **masculine:** männlich; Maskulinum.
8 f. **contestant:** Gegner(in).
10 **feminine:** weiblich; Femininum.
11 **to withhold:** versagen, vorenthalten.
23 **bonito** (pl. *bonita*) (Span.): Blaufisch.
   albacore (Span.): Albacore (Gattung der Thunfische).

drifting with the current. One bait was down forty fathoms. The second was at seventy-five and the third and
fourth were down in the blue water at one hundred and
one hundred and twenty-five fathoms. Each bait hung
5 head down with the shank of the hook inside the bait
fish, tied and sewed solid, and all the projecting part of
the hook, the curve and the point, was covered with
fresh sardines. Each sardine was hooked through both
eyes so that they made a half-garland on the projecting
10 steel. There was no part of the hook that a great fish
could feel which was not sweet-smelling and good-tast-
ing.

The boy had given him two fresh small tunas, or al-
bacores, which hung on the two deepest lines like
15 plummets and, on the others, he had a big blue runner
and a yellow jack that had been used before; but they
were in good condition still and had the excellent sardines to give them scent and attractiveness. Each line,
as thick around as a big pencil, was looped onto a
20 green-sapped stick so that any pull or touch on the bait
would make the stick dip and each line had two forty-
fathom coils which could be made fast to the other

---

5 **shank:** Schaft.
6 **to sew solid:** festnähen.
9 **half-garland:** Halbgirlande.
13 **tuna:** Thunfisch.
15 **plummet:** Bleigewicht, -senker.
   runner: Goldstöcker (tropischer Fisch).
16 **jack:** Stachelmakrele.
18 **attractiveness:** Attraktivität, Reiz.
19 **to loop:** schlingen, binden.
20 **green-sapped:** grün und saftig.
21 **to dip:** eindippen, -tauchen.
22 **coil:** Rolle.

spare coils so that, if it were necessary, a fish could take out over three hundred fathoms of line.

Now the man watched the dip of the three sticks over the side of the skiff and rowed gently to keep the lines straight up and down and at their proper depths. It was quite light and any moment now the sun would rise.

The sun rose thinly from the sea and the old man could see the other boats, low on the water and well in toward the shore, spread out across the current. Then the sun was brighter and the glare came on the water and then, as it rose clear, the flat sea sent it back at his eyes so that it hurt sharply and he rowed without looking into it. He looked down into the water and watched the lines that went straight down into the dark of the water. He kept them straighter than anyone did, so that at each level in the darkness of the stream there would be a bait waiting exactly where he wished it to be for any fish that swam there. Others let them drift with the current and sometimes they were at sixty fathoms when the fishermen thought they were at a hundred.

But, he thought, I keep them with precision. Only I have no luck any more. But who knows? Maybe today. Every day is a new day. It is better to be lucky. But I would rather be exact. Then when luck comes you are ready.

The sun was two hours higher now and it did not hurt his eyes so much to look into the east. There were only three boats in sight now and they showed very low and far inshore.

All my life the early sun has hurt my eyes, he

---

10 **glare:** Glast, Gleißen, greller Schein.
29 **inshore:** zur Küste hin, unter Land.

thought. Yet they are still good. In the evening I can look straight into it without getting the blackness. It has more force in the evening too. But in the morning it is painful.

5 Just then he saw a man-of-war bird with his long black wings circling in the sky ahead of him. He made a quick drop, slanting down on his back-swept wings, and then circled again.

"He's got something," the old man said aloud. "He's
10 not just looking."

He rowed slowly and steadily toward where the bird was circling. He did not hurry and he kept his lines straight up and down. But he crowded the current a little so that he was still fishing correctly though faster
15 than he would have fished if he was not trying to use the bird.

The bird went higher in the air and circled again, his wings motionless. Then he dove suddenly and the old man saw flying fish spurt out of the water and sail des-
20 perately over the surface.

"Dolphin," the old man said aloud. "Big dolphin."

He shipped his oars and brought a small line from under the bow. It had a wire leader and a medium-sized hook and he baited it with one of the sardines. He let

---

5 **man-of-war bird:** Fregattvogel.
6 f. **to make a drop:** sich fallen lassen, hinunterstoßen.
7 **to slant down:** sich neigen, schräg nach unten fliegen, gleiten.
   back-swept: hier: angelegt, pfeilförmig.
13 **to crowd the current:** die Fahrt beschleunigen, Tempo zulegen.
18 **dove:** *dived.*
19 **to spurt out:** heraus-, hervorspritzen.
22 **to ship the oars:** die Riemen einziehen.
23 **leader:** Öse.
24 **to bait:** beködern, mit einem Köder versehen.

it go over the side and then made it fast to a ring bolt
in the stern. Then he baited another line and left it
coiled in the shade of the bow. He went back to rowing
and to watching the long-winged black bird who was
5 working, now, low over the water.

As he watched the bird dipped again slanting his
wings for the dive and then swinging them wildly and
ineffectually as he followed the flying fish. The old
man could see the slight bulge in the water that the
10 big dolphin raised as they followed the escaping fish.
The dolphin were cutting through the water below
the flight of the fish and would be in the water, driving at speed, when the fish dropped. It is a big school
of dolphin, he thought. They are wide spread and the
15 flying fish have little chance. The bird has no chance.
The flying fish are too big for him and they go too
fast.

He watched the flying fish burst out again and again
and the ineffectual movements of the bird. That school
20 has gotten away from me, he thought. They are moving
out too fast and too far. But perhaps I will pick up a
stray and perhaps my big fish is round them. My big
fish must be somewhere.

The clouds over the land now rose like mountains
25 and the coast was only a long green line with the grey-
blue hills behind it. The water was a dark blue now, so

1 **ring bolt:** Ringbolzen.
6 **to slant:** schrägen, anlegen.
7 **dive:** Tauchen.
8 **ineffectually** (adv.): erfolg-, wirkungslos.
9 **bulge:** Ausbuchtung, Schwellung.
12 f. **to drive:** dahinjagen.
22 **stray:** hier: Nachzügler.

dark that it was almost purple. As he looked down into
it he saw the red sifting of the plankton in the dark water and the strange light the sun made now. He watched
his lines to see them go straight down out of sight into
5 the water and he was happy to see so much plankton
because it meant fish. The strange light the sun made in
the water, now that the sun was higher, meant good
weather and so did the shape of the clouds over the
land. But the bird was almost out of sight now and
10 nothing showed on the surface of the water but some
patches of yellow, sun-bleached Sargasso weed and the
purple, formalized, iridescent, gelatinous bladder of a
Portuguese man-of-war floating close beside the boat.
It turned on its side and then righted itself. It floated
15 cheerfully as a bubble with its long deadly purple filaments trailing a yard behind it in the water.

"Agua mala," the man said. "You whore."

From where he swung lightly against his oars he
looked down into the water and saw the tiny fish that

---

1 **purple:** violett.
2 **sifting:** Rückstände.
11 **sun-bleached:** sonnengebleicht.
   Sargasso weed: Beerentang.
12 **formalized:** fest geformt.
   iridescent: irisierend, schillernd.
   gelatinous: gallertartig.
   bladder: Blase.
13 **Portuguese man-of-war:** Portugiesische Galeere (Gattung der
   Quallen).
14 **to right o.s.:** sich aufrichten.
15 f. **filament:** Nesselfaden.
16 **to trail:** (hinterher)schweben, -gleiten.
17 **agua mala** (Span.): Qualle (wörtl.: böses Wasser).
   whore: Hure.

were coloured like the trailing filaments and swam between them and under the small shade the bubble made as it drifted. They were immune to its poison. But men were not and when some of the filaments would
5 catch on a line and rest there slimy and purple while the old man was working a fish, he would have welts and sores on his arms and hands of the sort that poison ivy or poison oak can give. But these poisonings from the *agua mala* came quickly and struck like a whiplash.

10 The iridescent bubbles were beautiful. But they were the falsest things in the sea and the old man loved to see the big sea turtles eating them. The turtles saw them, approached them from the front, then shut their eyes so they were completely carapaced and ate them
15 filaments and all. The old man loved to see the turtles eat them and he loved to walk on them on the beach after a storm and hear them pop when he stepped on them with the horny soles of his feet.

He loved green turtles and hawks-bills with their elegance
20 and speed and their great value and he had a friendly contempt for the huge, stupid logger-heads,

---

5 **slimy:** schleimig.
6 **to work** (auch: *to work on*) **a fish:** einen Fisch (an der Angel) zappeln lassen, drillen.
  welt: Strieme(n).
7 f. **poison ivy:** Giftefeu.
9 **whiplash:** Peitschenhieb.
12 **sea turtle:** Seeschildkröte.
14 **carapaced:** gepanzert (Schildkröte).
18 **horny:** hornig.
  sole: (Fuß-)Sohle.
19 **green turtle:** Suppenschildkröte.
  hawks-bill: Echte Karettschildkröte.
21 **logger-head:** Unechte Karettschildkröte.

yellow in their armour-plating, strange in their love-making, and happily eating the Portuguese men-of-war with their eyes shut.

He had no mysticism about turtles although he had gone in turtle boats for many years. He was sorry for them all, even the great trunk-backs that were as long as the skiff and weighed a ton. Most people are heartless about turtles because a turtle's heart will beat for hours after he has been cut up and butchered. But the old man thought, I have such a heart too and my feet and hands are like theirs. He ate the white eggs to give himself strength. He ate them all through May to be strong in September and October for the truly big fish.

He also drank a cup of shark liver oil each day from the big drum in the shack where many of the fishermen kept their gear. It was there for all fishermen who wanted it. Most fishermen hated the taste. But it was no worse than getting up at the hours that they rose and it was very good against all colds and grippes and it was good for the eyes.

Now the old man looked up and saw that the bird was circling again.

"He's found fish," he said aloud. No flying fish broke the surface and there was no scattering of bait fish. But as the old man watched, a small tuna rose in the air, turned and dropped head first into the water. The tuna shone silver in the sun and after he had dropped back

---

1 **armour-plating:** Panzerung.
1 f. **love-making:** Liebesspiel.
4 **mysticism:** Mystizismus, Mystik.
6 **trunk-back:** Lederschildkröte.
7 f. **heartless:** herzlos, grausam.

into the water another and another rose and they were
jumping in all directions, churning the water and leap-
ing in long jumps after the bait. They were circling it
and driving it.

5   If they don't travel too fast I will get into them, the
old man thought, and he watched the school working
the water white and the bird now dropping and dipping
into the bait fish that were forced to the surface in their
panic.

10   "The bird is a great help," the old man said. Just then
the stern line came taut under his foot, where he had
kept a loop of the line, and he dropped his oars and felt
the weight of the small tuna's shivering pull as he held
the line firm and commenced to haul it in. The shiver-
15 ing increased as he pulled in and he could see the blue
back of the fish in the water and the gold of his sides
before he swung him over the side and into the boat.
He lay in the stern in the sun, compact and bullet-
shaped, his big, unintelligent eyes staring as he
20 thumped his life out against the planking of the boat
with the quick shivering strokes of his neat, fast-moving
tail. The old man hit him on the head for kindness and
kicked him, his body still shuddering, under the shade
of the stern.

---

2 **to churn:** aufwühlen, peitschen.
6 **to work:** hier: aufschäumen, quirlen.
11 **to come taut:** sich spannen, straffen (*taut:* straff, gespannt).
12 **loop:** Bucht, Schleife, Schlinge (in einem Tau, einer Leine).
14 **to commence:** anfangen, beginnen.
18f. **bullet-shaped:** kugelförmig.
20 **to thump one's life out:** (durch Schläge) sein Leben aushauchen.
   planking: Planken.
23 **to shudder:** zittern, zucken.

30

"Albacore," he said aloud. "He'll make a beautiful bait. He'll weigh ten pounds."

He did not remember when he had first started to talk aloud when he was by himself. He had sung when he was by himself in the old days and he had sung at night sometimes when he was alone steering on his watch in the smacks or in the turtle boats. He had probably started to talk aloud, when alone, when the boy had left. But he did not remember. When he and the boy fished together they usually spoke only when it was necessary. They talked at night or when they were storm-bound by bad weather. It was considered a virtue not to talk unnecessarily at sea and the old man had always considered it so and respected it. But now he said his thoughts aloud many times since there was no one that they could annoy.

"If the others heard me talking out loud they would think that I am crazy," he said aloud. "But since I am not crazy, I do not care. And the rich have radios to talk to them in their boats and to bring them the baseball."

Now is no time to think of baseball, he thought. Now is the time to think of only one thing. That which I was born for. There might be a big one around that school, he thought. I picked up only a straggler from the albacore that were feeding. But they are working far out and fast. Everything that shows on the surface today travels very fast and to the north-east. Can that be the

---

7 **smack:** Schmack(e) (kleines Seeschiff).
12 **storm-bound:** vom Sturm am Auslaufen gehindert.
13 **unnecessarily** (adv.): überflüssigerweise.
25 **straggler:** Nachzügler.

time of day? Or is it some sign of weather that I do not know?

He could not see the green of the shore now but only the tops of the blue hills that showed white as though they were snow-capped and the clouds that looked like high snow mountains above them. The sea was very dark and the light made prisms in the water. The myriad flecks of the plankton were annulled now by the high sun and it was only the great deep prisms in the blue water that the old man saw now with his lines going straight down into the water that was a mile deep.

The tuna, the fishermen called all the fish of that species tuna and only distinguished among them by their proper names when they came to sell them or to trade them for baits, were down again. The sun was hot now and the old man felt it on the back of his neck and felt the sweat trickle down his back as he rowed.

I could just drift, he thought, and sleep and put a bight of line around my toe to wake me. But today is eighty-five days and I should fish the day well.

Just then, watching his lines, he saw one of the projecting green sticks dip sharply.

"Yes," he said. "Yes," and shipped his oars without bumping the boat. He reached out for the line and held

5 **snow-capped:** schneebedeckt.
7 **to make prisms:** sich brechen.
  myriad: Myriade; unzählig, zahllos.
8 **fleck:** Fleck, Sprenkel, Tupfen, Tupfer.
  to annul: (aus)löschen.
12f. **species:** Spezies, Art, Gattung.
17 **to trickle:** rieseln, rinnen.
19 **bight:** Bucht, Schleife, Schlinge (in einem Tau, einer Leine).
24 **to bump:** rammen, stoßen.
  to reach out for s.th.: nach etwas greifen, langen.

it softly between the thumb and forefinger of his right hand. He felt no strain nor weight and he held the line lightly. Then it came again. This time it was a tentative pull, not solid nor heavy, and he knew exactly what it
5 was. One hundred fathoms down a marlin was eating the sardines that covered the point and the shank of the hook where the hand-forged hook projected from the head of the small tuna.

The old man held the line delicately, and softly, with
10 his left hand, unleashed it from the stick. Now he could let it run through his fingers without the fish feeling any tension.

This far out, he must be huge in this month, he thought. Eat them, fish. Eat them. Please eat them.
15 How fresh they are and you down there six hundred feet in that cold water in the dark. Make another turn in the dark and come back and eat them.

He felt the light delicate pulling and then a harder pull when a sardine's head must have been more diffi-
20 cult to break from the hook. Then there was nothing.

"Come on," the old man said aloud. "Make another turn. Just smell them. Aren't they lovely? Eat them good now and then there is the tuna. Hard and cold and lovely. Don't be shy, fish. Eat them."
25 He waited with the line between his thumb and his finger, watching it and the other lines at the same time for the fish might have swum up or down. Then came the same delicate pulling touch again.

---

1 **forefinger:** Zeigefinger.
2 **strain:** Druck, Spannung.
3 **tentative:** vorsichtig, zaghaft, zögernd.
7 **hand-forged:** handgeschmiedet.
10 **to unleash:** losbinden.

"He'll take it," the old man said aloud. "God help him to take it."

He did not take it though. He was gone and the old man felt nothing.

5 "He can't have gone," he said. "Christ knows he can't have gone. He's making a turn. Maybe he has been hooked before and he remembers something of it."

Then he felt the gentle touch on the line and he was happy.

10 "It was only his turn," he said. "He'll take it."

He was happy feeling the gentle pulling and then he felt something hard and unbelievably heavy. It was the weight of the fish and he let the line slip down, down, down, unrolling off the first of the two reserve coils. As 15 it went down, slipping lightly through the old man's fingers, he still could feel the great weight, though the pressure of his thumb and finger were almost imperceptible.

"What a fish," he said. "He has it sideways in his 20 mouth now and he is moving off with it."

Then he will turn and swallow it, he thought. He did not say that because he knew that if you said a good thing it might not happen. He knew what a huge fish this was and he thought of him moving away in the 25 darkness with the tuna held crosswise in his mouth. At that moment he felt him stopping but the weight was still there. Then the weight increased and he gave more

---

1 **to take:** (Köder) annehmen, anbeißen.
12 **unbelievably** (adv.): unglaublich.
14 **to unroll s.th. off:** etwas abspulen, -wickeln.
17 f. **imperceptible:** nicht spürbar, kaum wahrnehmbar.
19 **sideways** (adv.): seitlich.
25 **crosswise** (adv.): quer.

line. He tightened the pressure of his thumb and finger for a moment and the weight increased and was going straight down.

"He's taken it," he said. "Now I'll let him eat it well."

5 He let the line slip through his fingers while he reached down with his left hand and made fast the free end of the two reserve coils to the loop of the two reserve coils of the next line. Now he was ready. He had three forty-fathom coils of line in reserve now, as well 10 as the coil he was using.

"Eat it a little more," he said. "Eat it well."

Eat it so that the point of the hook goes into your heart and kills you, he thought. Come up easy and let me put the harpoon into you. All right. Are you ready? 15 Have you been long enough at table?

"Now!" he said aloud and struck hard with both hands, gained a yard of line and then struck again and again, swinging with each arm alternately on the cord with all the strength of his arms and the pivoted weight 20 of his body.

Nothing happened. The fish just moved away slowly and the old man could not raise him an inch. His line was strong and made for heavy fish and he held it against his back until it was so taut that beads of water 25 were jumping from it. Then it began to make a slow hissing sound in the water and he still held it, bracing himself against the thwart and leaning back against the

---

1 **to tighten:** verstärken.
6 **to make fast:** festmachen, befestigen.
18 **with each arm alternately:** Hand über Hand.
19 **to pivot:** drehen, schwenken.
24 **bead:** Perle.
26 f. **to brace o.s.:** sich stemmen.

pull. The boat began to move slowly off toward the north-west.

The fish moved steadily and they travelled slowly on the calm water. The other baits were still in the water
5 but there was nothing to be done.

"I wish I had the boy," the old man said aloud. "I'm being towed by a fish and I'm the towing bitt. I could make the line fast. But then he could break it. I must hold him all I can and give him line when he must have
10 it. Thank God he is travelling and not going down."

What I will do if he decides to go down, I don't know. What I'll do if he sounds and dies I don't know. But I'll do something. There are plenty of things I can do.

He held the line against his back and watched its
15 slant in the water and the skiff moving steadily to the north-west.

This will kill him, the old man thought. He can't do this for ever. But four hours later the fish was still swimming steadily out to sea, towing the skiff, and the
20 old man was still braced solidly with the line across his back.

"It was noon when I hooked him," he said. "And I have never seen him."

He had pushed his straw hat hard down on his head
25 before he hooked the fish and it was cutting his fore-head. He was thirsty too and he got down on his knees and, being careful not to jerk on the line, moved as far

---

7 **to tow:** schleppen, in Schlepp nehmen.
  bitt: Beting, Poller (zum Befestigen der Schlepptrosse).
12 **to sound:** auf Grund, in die Tiefe gehen.
15 **slant:** Neigung, Schräge.
27 **to jerk:** rucken, zucken.

36

into the bow as he could get and reached the water bottle with one hand. He opened it and drank a little. Then he rested against the bow. He rested sitting on the unstepped mast and sail and tried not to think but only to endure.

Then he looked behind him and saw that no land was visible. That makes no difference, he thought. I can always come in on the glow from Havana. There are two more hours before the sun sets and maybe he will come up before that. If he doesn't maybe he will come up with the moon. If he does not do that maybe he will come up with the sunrise. I have no cramps and I feel strong. It is he that has the hook in his mouth. But what a fish to pull like that. He must have his mouth shut tight on the wire. I wish I could see him. I wish I could see him only once to know what I have against me.

The fish never changed his course nor his direction all that night as far as the man could tell from watching the stars. It was cold after the sun went down and the old man's sweat dried cold on his back and his arms and his old legs. During the day he had taken the sack that covered the bait box and spread it in the sun to dry. After the sun went down he tied it around his neck so that it hung down over his back and he cautiously worked it down under the line that was across his shoulders now. The sack cushioned the line and he had found a way of leaning forward against the bow so that he was almost

---

4 **to unstep:** (Mast) ausnehmen, niederlegen.
8 **glow:** Lichtschein.
12 **cramp:** Krampf.
24 f. **to work s.th. down under s.th. else:** etwas unter eine andere Sache schieben.

comfortable. The position actually was only somewhat less intolerable; but he thought of it as almost comfortable.

I can do nothing with him and he can do nothing
5 with me, he thought. Not as long as he keeps this up.

Once he stood up and urinated over the side of the skiff and looked at the stars and checked his course. The line showed like a phosphorescent streak in the
10 water straight out from his shoulders. They were moving more slowly now and the glow of Havana was not so strong, so that he knew the current must be carrying them to the eastward. If I lose the glare of Havana we must be going more to the eastward, he thought. For if
15 the fish's course held true I must see it for many more hours. I wonder how the baseball came out in the grand leagues today, he thought. It would be wonderful to do this with a radio. Then he thought, think of it always. Think of what you are doing. You must do nothing stu-
20 pid.

Then he said aloud, "I wish I had the boy. To help me and to see this."

No one should be alone in their old age, he thought. But it is unavoidable. I must remember to eat the tuna
25 before he spoils in order to keep strong. Remember, no matter how little you want to, that you must eat him in the morning. Remember, he said to himself.

---

2 **intolerable:** unerträglich.
9 **phosphorescent:** phosphoreszierend.
  streak: Streifen, Strich.
13 **to the eastward:** ostwärts, in östlicher Richtung.
15 **to hold true:** gleich bleiben.

During the night two porpoise came around the boat and he could hear them rolling and blowing. He could tell the difference between the blowing noise the male made and the sighing blow of the female.

"They are good," he said. "They play and make jokes and love one another. They are our brothers like the flying fish."

Then he began to pity the great fish that he had hooked. He is wonderful and strange and who knows how old he is, he thought. Never have I had such a strong fish nor one who acted so strangely. Perhaps he is too wise to jump. He could ruin me by jumping or by a wild rush. But perhaps he has been hooked many times before and he knows that this is how he should make his fight. He cannot know that it is only one man against him, nor that it is an old man. But what a great fish he is and what he will bring in the market if the flesh is good. He took the bait like a male and he pulls like a male and his fight has no panic in it. I wonder if he has any plans or if he is just as desperate as I am?

He remembered the time he had hooked one of a pair of marlin. The male fish always let the female fish feed first and the hooked fish, the female, made a wild, panic-stricken, despairing fight that soon exhausted her, and all the time the male had stayed with her, crossing the line and circling with her on the surface. He had stayed so close that the old man was afraid he would cut the line with his tail which was sharp as a scythe and almost of that size and shape. When the old

---

1 **porpoise:** Tümmler.
24 **panic-stricken:** angsterfüllt, von Panik erfasst.
29 **scythe:** Sense.

man had gaffed her and clubbed her, holding the rapier bill with its sandpaper edge and clubbing her across the top of her head until her colour turned to a colour almost like the backing of mirrors, and then, with the boy's aid, hoisted her aboard, the male fish had stayed by the side of the boat. Then, while the old man was clearing the lines and preparing the harpoon, the male fish jumped high into the air beside the boat to see where the female was and then went down deep, his lavender wings, that were his pectoral fins, spread wide and all his wide lavender stripes showing. He was beautiful, the old man remembered, and he had stayed.

That was the saddest thing I ever saw with them, the old man thought. The boy was sad too and we begged her pardon and butchered her promptly.

"I wish the boy was here," he said aloud and settled himself against the rounded planks of the bow and felt the strength of the great fish through the line he held across his shoulders moving steadily toward whatever he had chosen.

When once, through my treachery, it had been necessary to him to make a choice, the old man thought.

---

1 **to gaff:** mit dem Fischhaken ins Boot ziehen.
1 f. **rapier:** rapierähnlich (*rapier:* Rapier [degenartige Fechtwaffe]).
2 **bill:** Schnabel, Schnauze.
 sandpaper: Sand-, Schmirgelpapier.
4 **backing:** (Spiegel-)Rückwand, Silberschicht.
5 **to hoist:** heben, hieven, wuchten.
10 **lavender:** lavendelfarben.
 pectoral fin: Brustflosse.
17 f. **to settle o.s.:** hier: sich lehnen.
22 **treachery:** Hinterlist, Niedertracht, Tücke.

40

His choice had been to stay in the deep dark water far out beyond all snares and traps and treacheries. My choice was to go there to find him beyond all people. Beyond all people in the world. Now we are joined together and have been since noon. And no one to help either one of us.

Perhaps I should not have been a fisherman, he thought. But that was the thing that I was born for. I must surely remember to eat the tuna after it gets light.

Some time before daylight something took one of the baits that were behind him. He heard the stick break and the line begin to rush out over the gunwale of the skiff. In the darkness he loosened his sheath knife and taking all the strain of the fish on his left shoulder he leaned back and cut the line against the wood of the gunwale. Then he cut the other line closest to him and in the dark made the loose ends of the reserve coils fast. He worked skilfully with the one hand and put his foot on the coils to hold them as he drew his knots tight. Now he had six reserve coils of line. There were two from each bait he had severed and the two from the bait the fish had taken and they were all connected.

After it is light, he thought, I will work back to the forty-fathom bait and cut it away too and link up the reserve coils. I will have lost two hundred fathoms of

---

2 **snare:** Schlinge.
12 **to rush out:** davonrasen, -sausen.
   gunwale: Dollbord.
13 f. **sheath knife:** in einer Scheide steckendes Messer (*sheath:* [Waffen-]Scheide).
21 **to sever:** abtrennen, durchschneiden.

good Catalan *cordel* and the hooks and leaders. That can be replaced. But who replaces this fish if I hook some fish and it cuts him off? I don't know what that fish was that took the bait just now. It could have been a marlin or a broadbill or a shark. I never felt him. I had to get rid of him too fast.

Aloud he said, "I wish I had the boy."

But you haven't got the boy, he thought. You have only yourself and you had better work back to the last line now, in the dark or not in the dark, and cut it away and hook up the two reserve coils.

So he did it. It was difficult in the dark and once the fish made a surge that pulled him down on his face and made a cut below his eye. The blood ran down his cheek a little way. But it coagulated and dried before it reached his chin and he worked his way back to the bow and rested against the wood. He adjusted the sack and carefully worked the line so that it came across a new part of his shoulders and, holding it anchored with his shoulders, he carefully felt the pull of the fish and then felt with his hand the progress of the skiff through the water.

I wonder what he made that lurch for, he thought. The wire must have slipped on the great hill of his back. Certainly his back cannot feel as badly as mine does. But he cannot pull this skiff for ever, no matter

---

1 **Catalan:** katalanisch.
  cordel (Span.): Kordel, Leine, Seil.
5 **broadbill:** Schwertfisch.
13 **surge:** (hohe) Welle, Woge.
15 **to coagulate:** gerinnen.
19 **to anchor:** verankern.
23 **lurch:** Ruck.

how great he is. Now everything is cleared away that
might make trouble and I have a big reserve of line; all
that a man can ask.

"Fish," he said softly, aloud, "I'll stay with you until
I am dead."

He'll stay with me too, I suppose, the old man
thought and he waited for it to be light. It was cold now
in the time before daylight and he pushed against the
wood to be warm. I can do it as long as he can, he
thought. And in the first light the line extended out and
down into the water. The boat moved steadily and
when the first edge of the sun rose it was on the old
man's right shoulder.

"He's headed north," the old man said. The current
will have set us far to the eastward, he thought. I wish
he would turn with the current. That would show that
he was tiring.

When the sun had risen further the old man realized
that the fish was not tiring. There was only one favour-
able sign. The slant of the line showed he was swimming at a lesser depth. That did not necessarily mean
that he would jump. But he might.

"God let him jump," the old man said. "I have
enough line to handle him."

Maybe if I can increase the tension just a little it will
hurt him and he will jump, he thought. Now that it
is daylight let him jump so that he'll fill the sacs along
his backbone with air and then he cannot go deep to
die.

He tried to increase the tension, but the line had

27 **sac:** Luftsack.
28 **backbone:** Rückgrat, Wirbelsäule.

been taut up to the very edge of the breaking point
since he had hooked the fish and he felt the harshness
as he leaned back to pull and knew he could put no
more strain on it. I must not jerk it ever, he thought.
5 Each jerk widens the cut the hook makes and then
when he does jump he might throw it. Anyway I feel
better with the sun and for once I do not have look
into it.

There was yellow weed on the line but the old man
10 knew that only made an added drag and he was
pleased. It was the yellow Gulf weed that had made so
much phosphorescence in the night.

"Fish," he said, "I love you and respect you very
much. But I will kill you dead before this day ends."
15 Let us hope so, he thought.

A small bird came toward the skiff from the north.
He was a warbler and flying very low over the water.
The old man could see that he was very tired.

The bird made the stern of the boat and rested there.
20 Then he flew around the old man's head and rested on
the line where he was more comfortable.

"How old are you?" the old man asked the bird. "Is
this your frist trip?"

The bird looked at him when he spoke. He was too
25 tired even to examine the line and he teetered on it as
his delicate feet gripped it fast.

---

1 **to taut up:** *to tauten up:* sich spannen, straffen.
  to the very edge of the breaking point: zum Zerreißen.
2 **harshness:** Härte.
5 **jerk:** Ruck.
  to widen: erweitern, vergrößern.
17 **warbler:** Grasmücke, Sänger (Vogel).
25 **to teeter:** schwanken, wanken; schaukeln, wippen.

"It's steady," the old man told him. "It's too steady. You shouldn't be that tired after a windless night. What are birds coming to?"

The hawks, he thought, that come out to sea to meet them. But he said nothing of this to the bird who could not understand him anyway and who would learn about the hawks soon enough.

"Take a good rest, small bird," he said. "Then go in and take your chance like any man or bird or fish."

It encouraged him to talk because his back had stiffened in the night and it hurt truly now.

"Stay at my house if you like, bird," he said. "I am sorry I cannot hoist the sail and take you in with the small breeze that is rising. But I am with a friend."

Just then the fish gave a sudden lurch that pulled the old man down on to the bow and would have pulled him overboard if he had not braced himself and given some line.

The bird had flown up when the line jerked and the old man had not even seen him go. He felt the line carefully with his right hand and noticed his hand was bleeding.

"Something hurt him then," he said aloud and pulled back on the line to see if he could turn the fish. But when he was touching the breaking point he held steady and settled back against the strain of the line.

"You're feeling it now, fish," he said. "And so, God knows, am I."

---

2 **windless:** windstill.
4 **hawk:** Bussard, Falke, Habicht, Weihe.
10 f. **to stiffen:** steif werden, sich versteifen.
13 **to hoist:** (Segel) hissen, setzen.

He looked around for the bird now because he would have liked him for company. The bird was gone.

You did not stay long, the man thought. But it is rougher where you are going until you make the shore.
5 How did I let the fish cut me with that one quick pull he made? I must be getting very stupid. Or perhaps I was looking at the small bird and thinking of him. Now I will pay attention to my work and then I must eat the tuna so that I will not have a failure of strength.

10 "I wish the boy were here and that I had some salt," he said aloud.

Shifting the weight of the line to his left shoulder and kneeling carefully he washed his hand in the ocean and held it there, submerged, for more than a minute
15 watching the blood trail away and the steady movement of the water against his hand as the boat moved.

"He has slowed much," he said.

The old man would have liked to keep his hand in the salt water longer but he was afraid of another sud-
20 den lurch by the fish and he stood up and braced himself and held his hand up against the sun. It was only a line burn that had cut his flesh. But it was in the working part of his hand. He knew he would need his hands before this was over and he did not like to be cut
25 before it started.

"Now," he said, when his hand had dried, "I must eat the small tuna. I can reach him with the gaff and eat him here in comfort."

He knelt down and found the tuna under the stern
30 with the gaff and drew it toward him keeping it clear of

14 **to submerge**: ein-, untertauchen.
15 **to trail away**: sich verlieren.

the coiled lines. Holding the line with his left shoulder again, and bracing on his left hand and arm, he took the tuna off the gaff hook and put the gaff back in place. He put one knee on the fish and cut strips of
5 dark red meat longitudinally from the back of the head to the tail. They were wedge-shaped strips and he cut them from next to the backbone down to the edge of the belly. When he had cut six strips he spread them out on the wood of the bow, wiped his knife on his
10 trousers, and lifted the carcass of the bonito by the tail and dropped it overboard.

"I don't think I can eat an entire one," he said and drew his knife across one of the strips. He could feel the steady hard pull of the line and his left hand was
15 cramped. It drew up tight on the heavy cord and he looked at it in disgust.

"What kind of a hand is that," he said. "Cramp then if you want. Make yourself into a claw. It will do you no good."
20 Come on, he thought and looked down into the dark water at the slant of the line. Eat it now and it will strengthen the hand. It is not the hand's fault and you have been many hours with the fish. But you can stay with him for ever. Eat the bonito now.
25 He picked up a piece and put it in his mouth and chewed it slowly. It was not unpleasant.

Chew it well, he thought, and get all the juices. It

---

5 **longitudinally** (adv.): der Länge nach, längs.
6 **wedge-shaped:** keilförmig.
10 **carcass:** Aas, Kadaver; Gerippe, Skelett.
15 **cramped:** verkrampft.
16 **disgust:** Ekel, Abscheu.
18 **claw:** Klaue.

would not be bad to eat with a little lime or with lemon
or with salt.

"How do you feel, hand?" he asked the cramped
hand that was almost as stiff as rigor mortis. "I'll eat
5 some more for you."

He ate the other part of the piece that he had cut in
two. He chewed it carefully and then spat out the skin.

"How does it go, hand? Or is it too early to know?"

He took another full piece and chewed it.

10 "It is a strong full-blooded fish," he thought. "I was
lucky to get him instead of dolphin. Dolphin is too
sweet. This is hardly sweet at all and all the strength is
still in it."

There is no sense in being anything but practical
15 though, he thought. I wish I had some salt. And I do
not know whether the sun will rot or dry what is left, so
I had better eat it all although I am not hungry. The fish
is calm and steady. I will eat it all and then I will be
ready.

20 "Be patient, hand," he said. "I do this for you."

I wish I could feed the fish, he thought. He is my
brother. But I must kill him and keep strong to do it.
Slowly and conscientiously he ate all of the wedge-
shaped strips of fish.

25 He straightened up, wiping his hand on his trousers.

"Now," he said. "You can let the cord go, hand, and
I will handle him with the right arm alone until you
stop that nonsense." He put his left foot on the heavy

---

1 **lime:** Limone.
4 **rigor mortis** (Lat.): Todesstarre.
10 **full-blooded:** vollblütig.
25 **to straighten up:** sich aufrichten.
27 **to handle:** hier: (Fisch) drillen.

48

line that the left hand had held and lay back against the pull against his back.

"God help me to have the cramp go," he said. "Because I do not know what the fish is going to do."

5 But he seems calm, he thought, and following his plan. But what is his plan, he thought. And what is mine? Mine I must improvise to his because of his great size. If he will jump I can kill him. But he stays down for ever. Then I will stay down with him for ever.

10 He rubbed the cramped hand against his trousers and tried to gentle the fingers. But it would not open. Maybe it will open with the sun, he thought. Maybe it will open when the strong raw tuna is digested. If I have to have it, I will open it, cost whatever it costs. But 15 I do not want to open it now by force. Let it open by itself and come back of its own accord. After all I abused it much in the night when it was necessary to free and unite the various lines.

He looked across the sea and knew how alone he was 20 now. But he could see the prisms in the deep dark water and the line stretching ahead and the strange undulation of the calm. The clouds were building up now for the trade wind and he looked ahead and saw a flight of wild ducks etching themselves against the sky over the 25 water, then blurring, then etching again and he knew no man was ever alone on the sea.

7 **to improvise:** improvisieren.
11 **to gentle:** vorsichtig, behutsam bewegen.
21 f. **undulation:** Wellenbewegung, -spiel.
23 **trade wind:** Passatwind.
    flight: Flug, Schar, Zug.
24 **to etch o.s.:** sich abheben, abzeichnen.
25 **to blur:** verschwimmen, undeutlich werden.

He thought of how some men feared being out of
sight of land in a small boat and knew they were right
in the months of sudden bad weather. But now they
were in hurricane months and, when there are no hurri-
canes, the weather of hurricane months is the best of all
the year.

If there is a hurricane you always see the signs of it
in the sky for days ahead, if you are at sea. They do not
see it ashore because they do not know what to look
for, he thought. The land must make a difference too,
in the shape of the clouds. But we have no hurricane
coming now.

He looked at the sky and saw the white cumulus built
like friendly piles of ice cream and high above were the
thin feathers of the cirrus against the high September
sky.

"Light *brisa*," he said. "Better weather for me than
for you, fish."

His left hand was still cramped, but he was unknot-
ting it slowly.

I hate a cramp, he thought. It is a treachery of one's
own body. It is humiliating before others to have a diarrhoea from ptomaine poisoning or to vomit from it.

---

4 **hurricane:** Hurrikan, Orkan.
9 **ashore:** an Land.
13 **cumulus:** Kumulus-, Haufenwolke.
15 **cirrus:** Zirrus-, Federwolke.
17 **brisa** (Span.): Brise, Wind.
19 f. **to unknot:** hier: lockern.
22 **humiliating:** demütigend.
22 f. **diarrhoea:** Diarrhöe, Durchfall.
23 **ptomaine:** Ptomain, Leichengift.

But a cramp, he thought of it as a *calambre*, humiliates oneself especially when one is alone.

If the boy were here he could rub it for me and loosen it down from the forearm, he thought. But it will
5 loosen up.

Then, with his right hand he felt the difference in the pull of the line before he saw the slant change in the water. Then, as he leaned against the line and slapped his left hand hard and fast against his thigh he saw the
10 line slanting slowly upward.

"He's coming up," he said. "Come on, hand. Please come on."

The line rose slowly and steadily and then the surface of the ocean bulged ahead of the boat and the fish
15 came out. He came out unendingly and water poured from his sides. He was bright in the sun and his head and back were dark purple and in the sun the stripes on his sides showed wide and a light lavender. His sword was as long as a baseball bat and tapered like a rapier
20 and he rose his full length from the water and then re-entered it, smoothly, like a diver and the old man saw the great scythe-blade of his tail go under and the line commenced to race out.

---

1 **calambre** (Span.): Krampf.
4 **forearm:** Unterarm.
9 **thigh:** Oberschenkel.
14 **to bulge:** sich wölben.
15 **unendingly** (adv.): endlos.
18 **lavender**: Lavendelblau.
19 **bat:** (Baseball-)Schläger.
   to taper: sich verjüngen, spitz zulaufen.
21 **diver:** Taucher(in).
23 **to race out:** davonrasen, -sausen.

"He is two feet longer than the skiff," the old man said. The line was going out fast but steadily and the fish was not panicked. The old man was trying with both hands to keep the line just inside of breaking
5 strength. He knew that if he could not slow the fish with a steady pressure the fish could take out all the line and break it.

He is a great fish and I must convince him, he thought. I must never let him learn his strength nor
10 what he could do if he made his run. If I were him I would put in everything now and go until something broke. But, thank God, they are not as intelligent as we who kill them; although they are more noble and more able.

15 The old man had seen many great fish. He had seen many that weighed more than a thousand pounds and he had caught two of that size in his life, but never alone. Now alone, and out of sight of land, he was fast to the biggest fish that he had ever seen and bigger
20 than he had ever heard of, and his left hand was still as tight as the gripped claws of an eagle.

It will uncramp though, he thought. Surely it will uncramp to help my right hand. There are three things that are brothers: the fish and my two hands. It must
25 uncramp. It is unworthy of it to be cramped. The fish had slowed again and was going at his usual pace.

I wonder why he jumped, the old man thought. He jumped almost as though to show me how big he was.

---

10 **to make one's run:** das Weite suchen.
18f. **to be fast to s.th.:** an etwas gebunden, gefesselt sein.
22 **to uncramp:** sich entkrampfen.
25 **unworthy:** unwürdig.

I know now, anyway, he thought. I wish I could show him what sort of man I am. But then he would see the cramped hand. Let him think I am more man than I am and I will be so. I wish I was the fish, he thought, with
5 everything he has against only my will and my intelligence.

He settled comfortably against the wood and took his suffering as it came and the fish swam steadily and the boat moved slowly through the dark water. There
10 was a small sea rising with the wind coming up from the east and at noon the old man's left hand was uncramped.

"Bad news for you, fish," he said and shifted the line over the sack that covered his shoulders.

15 He was comfortable but suffering, although he did not admit the suffering at all.

"I am not religious," he said. "But I will say ten Our Fathers and ten Hail Marys that I should catch this fish, and I promise to make a pilgrimage to the Virgin de
20 Cobre if I catch him. That is a promise."

He commenced to say his prayers mechanically. Sometimes he would be so tired that he could not remember the prayer and then he would say them fast so that they would come automatically. Hail Marys are
25 easier to say than Our Fathers, he thought.

"Hail Mary full of Grace the Lord is with thee. Blessed art thou among women and blessed is the fruit

17 f. **Our Father:** Vaterunser.
18 **Hail Mary:** Ave Maria, Englischer Gruß (*to hail:* grüßen).
19 **pilgrimage:** Pilger-, Wallfahrt.
26 **thee** (arch.): *you.*
27 **art** (arch.): *are.*
  thou (arch.): *you.*

of thy womb, Jesus. Holy Mary, Mother of God, pray for us sinners now and at the hour of our death. Amen." Then he added, "Blessed Virgin, pray for the death of this fish. Wonderful though he is."

5 With his prayers said, and feeling much better, but suffering exactly as much, and perhaps a little more, he leaned against the wood of the bow and began, mechanically, to work the fingers of his left hand.

The sun was hot now although the breeze was rising
10 gently.

"I had better re-bait that little line out over the stern," he said. "If the fish decides to stay another night I will need to eat again and the water is low in the bottle. I don't think I can get anything but a dolphin here.
15 But if I eat him fresh enough he won't be bad. I wish a flying fish would come on board tonight. But I have no light to attract them. A flying fish is excellent to eat raw and I would not have to cut him up. I must save all my strength now. Christ, I did not know he was so big.
20 I'll kill him though," he said. "In all his greatness and his glory."

Although it is unjust, he thought. But I will show him what a man can do and what a man endures.

"I told the boy I was a strange old man," he said.
25 "Now is when I must prove it."

The thousand times that he had proved it meant nothing. Now he was proving it again. Each time was a new time and he never thought about the past when he was doing it.

---

1 **thy** (arch.): *your.*
  womb: Leib, Schoß.
11 **to re-bait:** neu beködern, mit einem neuen Köder versehen.

I wish he'd sleep and I could sleep and dream about the lions, he thought. Why are the lions the main thing that is left? Don't think, old man, he said to himself. Rest gently now against the wood and think of nothing. He

5 is working. Work as little as you can.

It was getting into the afternoon and the boat still moved slowly and steadily. But there was an added drag now from the easterly breeze and the old man rode gently with the small sea and the hurt of the cord

10 across his back came to him easily and smoothly.

Once in the afternoon the line started to rise again. But the fish only continued to swim at a slightly higher level. The sun was on the old man's left arm and shoulder and on his back. So he knew the fish had turned

15 east of north.

Now that he had seen him once, he could picture the fish swimming in the water with his purple pectoral fins set wide as wings and the great erect tail slicing through the dark. I wonder how much he sees at that depth, the

20 old man thought. His eye is huge and a horse, with much less eye, can see in the dark. Once I could see quite well in the dark. Not in the absolute dark. But almost as a cat sees.

The sun and his steady movement of his fingers had

25 uncramped his left hand now completely and he began to shift more of the strain to it and he shrugged the muscles of his back to shift the hurt of the cord a little.

---

8 **drag:** Hindernis, Erschwernis, Hemmnis.
   easterly: östlich.
9 **hurt:** Schmerz.
26 **to shrug:** zucken; hier: bewegen.

"If you're not tired, fish," he said aloud, "you must be very strange."

He felt very tired now and he knew the night would come soon and he tried to think of other things. He thought of the Big Leagues, to him they were the *Gran Ligas*, and he knew that the Yankees of New York were playing the *Tigres* of Detroit.

This is the second day now that I do not know the result of the *juegos*, he thought. But I must have confidence and I must be worthy of the great DiMaggio who does all things perfectly even with the pain of the bone spur in his heel. What is a bone spur? he asked himself. *Un espuela de hueso*. We do not have them. Can it be as painful as the spur of a fighting cock in one's heel? I do not think I could endure that or the loss of the eye and of both eyes and continue to fight as the fighting cocks do. Man is not much beside the great birds and beasts. Still I would rather be that beast down there in the darkness of the sea.

"Unless sharks come," he said aloud. "If sharks come, God pity him and me."

Do you believe the great DiMaggio would stay with a fish as long as I will stay with this one? he thought. I am sure he would and more since he is young and strong. Also his father was a fisherman. But would the bone spur hurt him too much?

"I do not know," he said aloud. "I never had a bone spur."

---

7 **Tigres** (Span., pl.): *Tigers*.
9 **juego** (Span.): Spiel.
11 f. **bone spur:** Knochensporn.
13 **un espuela de hueso** (Span.): Knochensporn.
14 **fighting cock:** Kampfhahn.

As the sun set he remembered, to give himself more confidence, the time in the tavern at Casablanca when he had played the hand game with the great negro from Cienfuegos who was the strongest man on the docks. They had gone one day and one night with their elbows on a chalk line on the table and their forearms straight up and their hands gripped tight. Each one was trying to force the other's hand down onto the table. There was much betting and people went in and out of the room under the kerosene lights and he had looked at the arm and hand of the negro and at the negro's face. They changed the referees every four hours after the first eight so that the referees could sleep. Blood came out from under the fingernails of both his and the negro's hands and they looked each other in the eye and at their hands and forearms and the bettors went in and out of the room and sat on high chairs against the wall and watched. The walls were painted bright blue and were of wood and the lamps threw their shadows against them. The negro's shadow was huge and it moved on the wall as the breeze moved the lamps.

The odds would change back and forth all night and they fed the negro rum and lighted cigarettes for him. Then the negro, after the rum, would try for a tremendous effort and once he had the old man, who was not

---

2 **tavern:** Taverne, Schenke.
3 **hand game:** Handdrücken (eine Art Fingerhakeln).
4 **Cienfuegos:** Hafenstadt in Zentralkuba.
10 **kerosene:** Kerosin.
16 **bettor:** Wettende(r), Wetter(in).
23 **odds:** Gewinn-, Wettchancen.
24 **to feed:** einflößen.

an old man then but was Santiago *El Campeón*, nearly three inches off balance. But the old man had raised his hand up to dead even again. He was sure then that he had the negro, who was a fine man and a great athlete,
5 beaten. And at daylight when the bettors were asking that it be called a draw and the referee was shaking his head, he had unleashed his effort and forced the hand of the negro down and down until it rested on the wood. The match had started on a Sunday morning and
10 ended on a Monday morning. Many of the bettors had asked for a draw because they had to go to work on the docks loading sacks of sugar or at the Havana Coal Company. Otherwise everyone would have wanted it to go to a finish. But he had finished it anyway and before
15 anyone had to go to work.

For a long time after that everyone had called him The Champion and there had been a return match in the spring. But not much money was bet and he had won it quite easily since he had broken the confidence
20 of the negro from Cienfuegos in the first match. After that he had a few matches and then no more. He decided that he could beat anyone if he wanted to badly enough and he decided that it was bad for his right hand for fishing. He had tried a few practice matches
25 with his left hand. But his left hand had always been a traitor and would not do what he called on it to do and he did not trust it.

1 **el campeón** (Span.): Champion; Kämpfer.
3 **to dead even:** zum völligen Ausgleich.
7 **to unleash** (fig.): entfesseln, freien Lauf lassen.
14 **to go to a finish:** bis zur Entscheidung weitergehen.
17 **return match:** Revanchekampf.
26 **traitor:** Verräter(in).

The sun will bake it out well now, he thought. It should not cramp on me again unless it gets too cold in the night. I wonder what this night will bring.

An aeroplane passed overhead on its course to Miami and he watched its shadow scaring up the schools of flying fish.

"With so much flying fish there should be dolphin," he said, and leaned back on the line to see if it was possible to gain any on his fish. But he could not and it stayed at the hardness and water-drop shivering that preceded breaking. The boat moved ahead slowly and he watched the aeroplane until he could no longer see it.

It must be very strange in an aeroplane, he thought. I wonder what the sea looks like from that height. They should be able to see the fish well if they do not fly too high. I would like to fly very slowly at two hundred fathoms high and see the fish from above. In the turtle boats I was in the cross-trees of the mast-head and even at that height I saw much. The dolphin look greener from there and you can see their stripes and their purple spots and you can see all of the school as they swim. Why is it that all the fast-moving fish of the dark current have purple backs and usually purple stripes or spots? The dolphin looks green of course because he is really golden. But when he comes to feed, truly hungry,

---

1 **to bake s.th. out:** etwas schmoren.
5 **to scare up:** aufscheuchen, -schrecken.
9 **to gain line on a fish:** einem Fisch Leine abgewinnen.
19 **cross-trees** (pl.): Dwarssaling (quer zum Schiffsmast befestigte Stange).
mast-head: Masttopp, -korb; Mars (Plattform an der Verlängerung eines Mastes).

purple stripes show on his sides as on a marlin. Can it be anger, or the greater speed he makes that brings them out?

Just before it was dark, as they passed a great island of Sargasso weed that heaved and swung in the light sea as though the ocean were making love with something under a yellow blanket, his small line was taken by a dolphin. He saw it first when it jumped in the air, true gold in the last of the sun and bending and flapping wildly in the air. It jumped again and again in the acrobatics of its fear and he worked his way back to the stern and crouching and holding the big line with his right hand and arm, he pulled the dolphin in with his left hand, stepping on the gained line each time with his bare left foot. When the fish was at the stern, plunging and cutting from side to side in desperation, the old man leaned over the stern and lifted the burnished gold fish with its purple spots over the stern. Its jaws were working convulsively in quick bites against the hook and it pounded the bottom of the skiff with its long flat body, its tail and its head until he clubbed it across the shining golden head until it shivered and was still.

The old man unhooked the fish, re-baited the line with another sardine and tossed it over. Then he worked his way slowly back to the bow. He washed his

---

5 **to heave:** auf und ab wogen.
9f. **to flap:** flappen, klatschen, schlagen.
11 **acrobatics** (pl.): Akrobatik, Trapezkunst.
12 **to crouch:** sich hinhocken, -kauern.
15 **to plunge:** (ein)tauchen.
17 **to burnish:** blank reiben, polieren.
19 **convulsively** (adv.): konvulsivisch, krampfhaft.
24 **to toss the line over:** die Leine auswerfen.

left hand and wiped it on his trousers. Then he shifted
the heavy line from his right hand to his left and
washed his right hand in the sea while he watched the
sun go into the ocean and the slant of the big cord.

5 "He hasn't changed at all," he said. But watching the
movement of the water against his hand he noted that
it was perceptibly slower.

"I'll lash the two oars together across the stern and
that will slow him in the night," he said. "He's good for
10 the night and so am I."

It would be better to gut the dolphin a little later to
save the blood in the meat, he thought. I can do that a
little later and lash the oars to make a drag at the same
time. I had better keep the fish quiet now and not dis-
15 turb him too much at sunset. The setting of the sun is
a difficult time for all fish.

He let his hand dry in the air then grasped the line
with it and eased himself as much as he could and al-
lowed himself to be pulled forward against the wood so
20 that the boat took the strain as much, or more, than he
did.

I'm learning how to do it, he thought. This part of it
anyway. Then too, remember he hasn't eaten since he
took the bait and he is huge and needs much food. I
25 have eaten the whole bonito. Tomorrow I will eat the
dolphin. He called it *dorado*. Perhaps I should eat some
of it when I clean it. It will be harder to eat than the bonito. But, then, nothing is easy.

---

7 **perceptibly** (adv.): merklich.
8 **to lash s.th. together:** etwas zusammenbinden.
11 **to gut:** ausnehmen, -weiden.
18 **to ease o.s.:** es sich bequem machen.
26 **dorado** (Span.): Goldmakrele.

"How do you feel, fish?" he asked aloud. "I feel good and my left hand is better and I have food for a night and a day. Pull the boat, fish."

He did not truly feel good because the pain from the
5 cord across his back had almost passed pain and gone into a dullness that he mistrusted. But I have had worse things than that, he thought. My hand is only cut a little and the cramp is gone from the other. My legs are all right. Also now I have gained on him in the question of
10 sustenance.

It was dark now as it becomes dark quickly after the sun sets in September. He lay against the worn wood of the bow and rested all that he could. The first stars were out. He did not know the name of Rigel but he
15 saw it and knew soon they would all be out and he would have all his distant friends.

"The fish is my friend too," he said aloud. "I have never seen or heard of such a fish. But I must kill him. I am glad we do not have to try to kill the stars."
20 Imagine if each day a man must try to kill the moon, he thought. The moon runs away. But imagine if a man each day should have to try to kill the sun? We were born lucky, he thought.

Then he was sorry for the great fish that had nothing
25 to eat and his determination to kill him never relaxed in his sorrow for him. How many people will he feed,

---

6 **dullness:** Benommenheit, Dumpfheit.
  to mistrust: misstrauen.
9 **to gain on s.o.:** jdm. überlegen sein.
10 **sustenance:** Nahrung, Ernährung.
14 **Rigel:** Rigel (Stern erster Größe im Orion).
26 **sorrow:** Kummer, Leid, Mitgefühl.

he thought. But are they worthy to eat him? No, of course not. There is no one worthy of eating him from the manner of his behaviour and his great dignity.

I do not understand these things, he thought. But it is good that we do not have to try to kill the sun or the moon or the stars. It is enough to live on the sea and kill our true brothers.

Now, he thought, I must think about the drag. It has its perils and its merits. I may lose so much line that I will lose him, if he makes his effort and the drag made by the oars is in place and the boat loses all her lightness. Her lightness prolongs both our suffering but it is my safety since he has great speed that he has never yet employed. No matter what passes I must gut the dolphin so he does not spoil and eat some of him to be strong.

Now I will rest an hour more and feel that he is solid and steady before I move back to the stern to do the work and make the decision. In the meantime I can see how he acts and if he shows any changes. The oars are a good trick; but it has reached the time to play for safety! He is much fish still and I saw that the hook was in the corner of his mouth and he has kept his mouth tight shut. The punishment of the hook is nothing. The punishment of hunger, and that he is against something that he does not comprehend, is everything. Rest now, old man, and let him work until your next duty comes.

He rested for what he believed to be two hours. The moon did not rise now until late and he had no way of

---

9 **peril:** Gefahr, Risiko.
19 **in the meantime:** in der Zwischenzeit, inzwischen.
26 **to comprehend:** begreifen, fassen, verstehen.

judging the time. Nor was he really resting except comparatively. He was still bearing the pull of the fish across his shoulders but he placed his left hand on the gunwale of the bow and confided more and more of the resistance to the fish to the skiff itself.

How simple it would be if I could make the line fast, he thought. But with one small lurch he could break it. I must cushion the pull of the line with my body and at all times be ready to give line with both hands.

"But you have not slept yet, old man," he said aloud. "It is half a day and a night and now another day and you have not slept. You must devise a way so that you sleep a little if he is quiet and steady. If you do not sleep you might become unclear in the head."

I'm clear enough in the head, he thought. Too clear. I am as clear as the stars that are my brothers. Still I must sleep. They sleep and the moon and the sun sleep and even the ocean sleeps sometimes on certain days when there is no current and a flat calm.

But remember to sleep, he thought. Make yourself do it and devise some simple and sure way about the lines. Now go back and prepare the dolphin. It is too dangerous to rig the oars as a drag if you must sleep.

I could go without sleeping, he told himself. But it would be too dangerous.

He started to work his way back to the stern on his hands and knees, being careful not to jerk against the fish. He may be half asleep himself, he thought. But I do not want him to rest. He must pull until he dies.

Back in the stern he turned so that his left hand held

---

4 **to confide:** anvertrauen, übertragen.
23 **to rig:** herrichten.

64

the strain of the line across his shoulders and drew his knife from its sheath with his right hand. The stars were bright now and he saw the dolphin clearly and he pushed the blade of his knife into his head and drew him out from under the stern. He put one of his feet on the fish and slit him quickly from the vent up to the tip of his lower jaw. Then he put his knife down and gutted him with his right hand, scooping him clean and pulling the gills clear. He felt the maw heavy and slippery in his hands and he slit it open. There were two flying fish inside. They were fresh and hard and he laid them side by side and dropped the guts and the gills over the stern. They sank leaving a trail of phosphorescence in the water. The dolphin was cold and a leprous grey-white now in the starlight and the old man skinned one side of him while he held his right foot on the fish's head. Then he turned him over and skinned the other side and cut each side off from the head down to the tail.

He slid the carcass overboard and looked to see if there was any swirl in the water. But there was only the light of its slow descent. He turned then and placed the two flying fish inside the two fillets of fish and putting his knife back in its sheath, he worked his way slowly

6 **to slit:** aufschlitzen.
  vent: After, Kloake.
8 **to scoop:** ausnehmen.
9 **gill:** Kieme.
  maw: Magen.
12 **guts:** Eingeweide, Gedärme.
13 **trail:** Spur, Fährte.
14 **leprous:** aussätzig, aussatzartig.
21 **descent:** Versinken.
22 **fillet:** Filet.

back to the bow. His back was bent with the weight of the line across it and he carried the fish in his right hand.

Back in the bow he laid the two fillets of fish out on
5 the wood with the flying fish beside them. After that he settled the line across his shoulders in a new place and held it again with his left hand resting on the gunwale. Then he leaned over the side and washed the flying fish in the water, noting the speed of the water
10 against his hand. His hand was phosphorescent from skinning the fish and he watched the flow of the water against it. The flow was less strong and as he rubbed the side of his hand against the planking of the skiff, particles of phosphorus floated off and drifted slowly
15 astern.

"He is tiring or he is resting," the old man said. "Now let me get through the eating of this dolphin and get some rest and a little sleep."

Under the stars and with the night colder all the time
20 he ate half of one of the dolphin fillets and one of the flying fish, gutted and with its head cut off.

"What an excellent fish dolphin is to eat cooked," he said. "And what a miserable fish raw. I will never go in a boat again without salt or limes."

25 If I had brains I would have splashed water on the bow all day and drying, it would have made salt, he thought. But then I did not hook the dolphin until al-

---

11 **flow:** Fluss, Strom, Strömung.
14 **particle:** Partikel, Teilchen.
   phosphorus: Phosphor.
15 **astern** (adv.): achtern, (nach) hinten.
25 **to splash:** spritzen.

most sunset. Still it was a lack of preparation. But I have chewed it all well and I am not nauseated.

The sky was clouding over to the east and one after another the stars he knew were gone. It looked now as though he were moving into a great canyon of clouds and the wind had dropped.

"There will be bad weather in three or four days," he said. "But not tonight and not tomorrow. Rig now to get some sleep, old man, while the fish is calm and steady."

He held the line tight in his right hand and then pushed his thigh against his right hand as he leaned all his weight against the wood of the bow. Then he passed the line a little lower on his shoulders and braced his left hand on it.

My right hand can hold it as long as it is braced, he thought. If it relaxes in sleep my left hand will wake me as the line goes out. It is hard on the right hand. But he is used to punishment. Even if I sleep twenty minutes of half an hour it is good. He lay forward cramping himself against the line with all of his body, putting all his weight on to his right hand, and he was asleep.

He did not dream of the lions but instead of a vast school of porpoise that stretched for eight or ten miles and it was in the time of their mating and they would leap high into the air and return into the same hole they had made in the water when they leaped.

---

2 **to nauseate:** Übelkeit erregen.
3 **to cloud over:** sich bewölken.
5 **canyon:** Cañon, Schlucht.
20 f. **to cramp o.s.:** sich drücken, klammern, pressen.
25 **mating:** Paarung.

Then he dreamed that he was in the village on his bed and there was a norther and he was very cold and his right arm was asleep because his head had rested on it instead of a pillow.

⁵ After that he began to dream of the long yellow beach and he saw the first of the lions come down onto it in the early dark and then the other lions came and he rested his chin on the wood of the bows where the ship lay anchored with the evening off-shore breeze ¹⁰ and he waited to see if there would be more lions and he was happy.

The moon had been up for a long time but he slept on and the fish pulled on steadily and the boat moved into the tunnel of clouds.

¹⁵ He woke with the jerk of his right fist coming up against his face and the line burning out through his right hand. He had no feeling of his left hand but he braked all he could with his right and the line rushed out. Finally his left hand found the line and he leaned ²⁰ back against the line and now it burned his back and his left hand, and his left hand was taking all the strain and cutting badly. He looked back at the coils of line and they were feeding smoothly. Just then the fish jumped making a great bursting of the ocean and then ²⁵ a heavy fall. Then he jumped again and again and the boat was going fast although line was still racing out and the old man was raising the strain to breaking point and raising it to breaking point again and again.

---

2 **norther:** Nordwind.
9 **to lay anchored:** vor Anker liegen.
  off-shore breeze: Landwind.
16 **to burn out:** glühend heiß davonrasen, -sausen.

He had been pulled down tight onto the bow and his face was in the cut slice of dolphin and he could not move.

This is what we waited for, he thought. So now let us take it.

Make him pay for the line, he thought. Make him pay for it.

He could not see the fish's jumps but only heard the breaking of the ocean and the heavy splash as he fell. The speed of the line was cutting his hands badly but he had always known this would happen and he tried to keep the cutting across the calloused parts and not let the line slip into the palm or cut the fingers.

If the boy was here he would wet the coils of line, he thought. Yes. If the boy were here. If the boy were here.

The line went out and out and out but it was slowing now and he was making the fish earn each inch of it. Now he got his head up from the wood and out of the slice of fish that his cheek had crushed. Then he was on his knees and then he rose slowly to his feet. He was ceding line but more slowly all the time. He worked back to where he could feel with his foot the coils of line that he could not see. There was plenty of line still and now the fish had to pull the friction of all that new line through the water.

Yes, he thought. And now he has jumped more than a dozen times and filled the sacs along his back with air and he cannot go down deep to die where I cannot

---

9 **splash:** Klatschen, Platschen.
12 **calloused:** schwielig.
22 **to cede line:** Leine abgeben.

bring him up. He will start circling soon and then I
must work on him. I wonder what started him so suddenly? Could it have been hunger that made him
desperate, or was he frightened by something in the
5 night? Maybe he suddenly felt fear. But he was such a
calm, strong fish and he seemed so fearless and so confident. It is strange.

"You better be fearless and confident yourself, old
man," he said. "You're holding him again but you can-
10 not get line. But soon he has to circle."

The old man held him with his left hand and his
shoulders now and stooped down and scooped up water in his right hand to get the crushed dolphin flesh off
of his face. He was afraid that it might nauseate him
15 and he would vomit and lose his strength. When his
face was cleaned he washed his right hand in the water
over the side and then let it stay in the salt water while
he watched the first light come before the sunrise. He's
headed almost east, he thought. That means he is tired
20 and going with the current. Soon he will have to circle.
Then our true work begins.

After he judged that his right hand had been in the
water long enough he took it out and looked at it.

"It is not bad," he said. "And pain does not matter to
25 a man."

He took hold of the line carefully so that it did not fit
into any of the fresh line cuts and shifted his weight so
that he could put his left hand into the sea on the other
side of the skiff.

---

6 **fearless:** furchtlos.
12 **to stoop down:** sich bücken.
   to scoop up: schöpfen.

"You did not do so badly for something worthless," he said to his left hand. "But there was a moment when I could not find you."

Why was I not born with two good hands? he thought. Perhaps it was my fault in not training that one properly. But God knows he has had enough chances to learn. He did not do so badly in the night, though, and he has only cramped once. If he cramps again let the line cut him off.

When he thought that he knew that he was not being clear-headed and he thought he should chew some more of the dolphin. But I can't, he told himself. It is better to be light-headed than to lose your strength from nausea. And I know I cannot keep it if I eat it since my face was in it. I will keep it for an emergency until it goes bad. But it is too late to try for strength now through nourishment. You're stupid, he told himself. Eat the other flying fish.

It was there, cleaned and ready, and he picked it up with his left hand and ate it chewing the bones carefully and eating all of it down to the tail.

It has more nourishment than almost any fish, he thought. At least the kind of strength that I need. Now I have done what I can, he thought. Let him begin to circle and let the fight come.

The sun was rising for the third time since he had put to sea when the fish started to circle.

---

1 **worthless:** wertlos.
11 **clear-headed:** klar denkend, besonnen.
13 **light-headed:** benommen; leichtfertig, -sinnig.
14 **nausea:** Übelkeit.
17 **nourishment:** Nahrung, Ernährung.

He could not see by the slant of the line that the fish was circling. It was too early for that. He just felt a faint slackening of the pressure of the line and he commenced to pull on it gently with his right hand. It tight-
5 ened, as always, but just when he reached the point where it would break, line began to come in. He slipped his shoulders and head from under the line and began to pull in line steadily and gently. He used both of his hands in a swinging motion and tried to do the
10 pulling as much as he could with his body and his legs. His old legs and shoulders pivoted with the swinging of the pulling.

"It is a very big circle," he said. "But he is circling."

Then the line would not come in any more and he
15 held it until he saw the drops jumping from it in the sun. Then it started out and the old man knelt down and let it go grudgingly back into the dark water.

"He is making the far part of his circle now," he said. I must hold all I can, he thought. The strain will shorten
20 his circle each time. Perhaps in an hour I will see him. Now I must convince him and then I must kill him.

But the fish kept on circling slowly and the old man was wet with sweat and tired deep into his bones two hours later. But the circles were much shorter now and
25 from the way the line slanted he could tell the fish had risen steadily while he swam.

For an hour the old man had been seeing black spots before his eyes and the sweat salted his eyes and salted the cut under his eye and on his forehead. He was not
30 afraid of the black spots. They were normal at the ten-

---

3 **to slacken:** nachlassen.
17 **grudgingly** (adv.): widerstrebend, -willig.

sion that he was pulling on the line. Twice, though, he had felt faint and dizzy and that had worried him.

"I could not fail myself and die on a fish like this," he said. "Now that I have him coming so beautifully, God help me endure. I'll say a hundred Our Fathers and a hundred Hail Marys. But I cannot say them now."

Consider them said, he thought. I'll say them later.

Just then he felt a sudden banging and jerking on the line he held with his two hands. It was sharp and hard-feeling and heavy.

He is hitting the wire leader with his spear, he thought. That was bound to come. He had to do that. It may make him jump though and I would rather he stayed circling now. The jumps were necessary for him to take air. But after that each one can widen the opening of the hook wound and he can throw the hook.

"Don't jump, fish," he said. "Don't jump."

The fish hit the wire several times more and each time he shook his head the old man gave up a little line.

I must hold his pain where it is, he thought. Mine does not matter. I can control mine. But his pain could drive him mad.

After a while the fish stopped beating at the wire and started circling slowly again. The old man was gaining line steadily now. But he felt faint again. He lifted some sea water with his left hand and put it on his head. Then he put more on and rubbed the back of his neck.

---

2 **dizzy:** schwindlig.
3 **to fail o.s.:** unterliegen.
9f. **hard-feeling:** hart.
11 **spear:** Speer; hier: Schwert.
12 **to be bound to do s.th.:** etwas tun müssen.

"I have no cramps," he said. "He'll be up soon and I can last. You have to last. Don't even speak of it."

He kneeled against the bow and, for a moment, slipped the line over his back again. I'll rest now while he goes out on the circle and then stand up and work on him when he comes in, he decided.

It was a great temptation to rest in the bow and let the fish make one circle by himself without recovering any line. But when the strain showed the fish had turned to come toward the boat, the old man rose to his feet and started the pivoting and the weaving pulling that brought in all the line he gained.

I'm tireder than I have ever been, he thought, and now the trade wind is rising. But that will be good to take him in with. I need that badly.

"I'll rest on the next turn as he goes out," he said. "I feel much better. Then in two or three turns more I will have him."

His straw hat was far on the back of his head and he sank down into the bow with the pull of the line as he felt the fish turn.

You work now, fish, he thought. I'll take you at the turn.

The sea had risen considerably. But it was a fair-weather breeze and he had to have it to get home.

"I'll just steer south and west," he said. "A man is never lost at sea and it is a long island."

It was on the third turn that he saw the fish first.

He saw him first as a dark shadow that took so long to pass under the boat that he could not believe its length.

"No," he said. "He can't be that big."

But he was that big and at the end of this circle he

came to the surface only thirty yards away and the man
saw his tail out of water. It was higher than a big scythe-
blade and a very pale lavender above the dark blue water. It raked back and as the fish swam just below the
surface the old man could see his huge bulk and the
purple stripes that banded him. His dorsal fin was
down and his huge pectorals were spread wide.

On this circle the old man could see the fish's eye and
the two grey sucking fish that swam around him. Sometimes they attached themselves to him. Sometimes they
darted off. Sometimes they would swim easily in his
shadow. They were each over three feet long and when
they swam fast they lashed their whole bodies like
eels.

The old man was sweating now but from something
else besides the sun. On each calm placid turn the fish
made he was gaining line and he was sure that in two
turns he would have a chance to get the harpoon in.

But I must get him close, close, close, he thought. I
mustn't try for the head. I must get the heart.

"Be calm and strong, old man," he said.

On the next circle the fish's back was out but he was
a little too far from the boat. On the next circle he was
still too far away but he was higher out of the water and

---

4 **to rake back:** hier: zurückfallen.
6 **to band:** umbinden, -gürten.
  dorsal fin: Rückenflosse.
7 **pectoral:** Brustflosse.
9 **sucking fish:** Schildfisch, Schiffshalter.
11 **to dart off:** davonschießen.
13 **to lash:** hin und her bewegen, schlagen, peitschen.
14 **eel:** Aal.
16 **placid:** gelassen, gemächlich.

the old man was sure that by gaining some more line he could have him alongside.

He had rigged his harpoon long before and its coil of light rope was in a round basket and the end was made
5 fast to the bitt in the bow.

The fish was coming in on his circle now calm and beautiful-looking and only his great tail moving. The old man pulled on him all that he could to bring him closer. For just a moment the fish turned a little on his
10 side. Then he straightened himself and began another circle.

"I moved him," the old man said. "I moved him then."

He felt faint again now but he held on the great fish
15 all the strain that he could. I moved him, he thought. Maybe this time I can get him over. Pull, hands, he thought. Hold up, legs. Last for me, head. Last for me. You never went. This time I'll pull him over.

But when he put all of his effort on, starting it well
20 out before the fish came alongside and pulling with all his strength, the fish pulled part way over and then righted himself and swam away.

"Fish," the old man said. "Fish, you are going to have to die anyway. Do you have to kill me too?"

25 That way nothing is accomplished, he thought. His mouth was too dry to speak but he could not reach for the water now. I must get him alongside this time, he thought. I am not good for many more turns. Yes you are, he told himself. You're good for ever.

30 On the next turn, he nearly had him. But again the fish righted himself and swam slowly away.

You are killing me, fish, the old man thought. But you have a right to. Never have I seen a greater, or

more beautiful, or a calmer or more noble thing than
you, brother. Come on and kill me. I dot not care who
kills who.

Now you are getting confused in the head, he
5 thought. You must keep your head clear. Keep your
head clear and know how to suffer like a man. Or a
fish, he thought.

"Clear up, head," he said in a voice he could hardly
hear. "Clear up."

10 Twice more it was the same on the turns.

I do not know, the old man thought. He had been on
the point of feeling himself go each time. I do not
know. But I will try it once more.

He tried it once more and he felt himself going when
15 he turned the fish. The fish righted himself and swam
off again slowly with the great tail weaving in the air.

I'll try it again, the old man promised, although his
hands were mushy now and he could only see well in
flashes.

20 He tried it again and it was the same. So, he thought,
and he felt himself going before he started; I will try it
once again.

He took all his pain and what was left of his strength
and his long-gone pride and he put it against the fish's
25 agony and the fish came over onto his side and swam
gently on his side, his bill almost touching the planking
of the skiff, and started to pass the boat, long, deep,
wide, silver and barred with purple and interminable in
the water.

18 **mushy:** wie Brei, zerquetscht.
25 **agony:** Agonie, Todeskampf.
28 **barred:** gestreift.
  interminable: endlos.

The old man dropped the line and put his foot on it
and lifted the harpoon as high as he could and drove it
down with all his strength, and more strength he had
just summoned, into the fish's side just behind the great
5 chest fin that rose high in the air to the altitude of the
man's chest. He felt the iron go in and he leaned on it
and drove it further and then pushed all his weight after it.

Then the fish came alive, with his death in him, and
10 rose high out of the water showing all his great length
and width and all his power and his beauty. He seemed
to hang in the air above the old man in the skiff. Then
he fell into the water with a crash that sent spray over
the old man and over all of the skiff.

15 The old man felt faint and sick and he could not see
well. But he cleared the harpoon line and let it run
slowly through his raw hands and, when he could see,
he saw the fish was on his back with his silver belly up.
The shaft of the harpoon was projecting at an angle
20 from the fish's shoulder and the sea was discolouring
with the red of the blood from his heart. First it was
dark as a shoal in the blue water that was more than a
mile deep. Then it spread like a cloud. The fish was silvery and still and floated with the waves.

25 The old man looked carefully in the glimpse of vision
that he had. Then he took two turns of the harpoon line

---

2 f. **to drive s.th. down:** etwas hinabstoßen.
4 **to summon:** aufbringen.
5 **altitude:** Höhe.
13 **spray:** Gischt, Schaum.
20 **to discolour:** sich verfärben.
22 **shoal:** Sandbank, Untiefe.
23 f. **silvery:** silbrig.

around the bitt in the bow and laid his head on his hands.

"Keep my head clear," he said against the wood of the bow. "I am a tired old man. But I have killed this fish which is my brother and now I must do the slave work."

Now I must prepare the nooses and the rope to lash him alongside, he thought. Even if we were two and swamped her to load him and bailed her out, this skiff would never hold him. I must prepare everything, then bring him in and lash him well and step the mast and set sail for home.

He started to pull the fish in to have him alongside so that he could pass a line through his gills and out his mouth and make his head fast alongside the bow. I want to see him, he thought, and to touch and to feel him. He is my fortune, he thought. But that is not why I wish to feel him. I think I felt his heart, he thought. When I pushed on the harpoon shaft the second time. Bring him in now and make him fast and get the noose around his tail and another around his middle to bind him to the skiff.

"Get to work, old man," he said. He took a very small drink of the water. "There is very much slave work to be done now that the fight is over."

He looked up at the sky and then out to his fish. He looked at the sun carefully. It is not much more than noon, he thought. And the trade wind is rising. The

---

7 **noose:** Schlinge.

   to lash: vertäuen, festbinden, -zurren.
9 **to swamp:** voll laufen lassen.

   to bail out: (Boot) ausschöpfen.
11 **to step:** (Mast) aufrichten.

lines all mean nothing now. The boy and I will splice them when we are home.

"Come on, fish," he said. But the fish did not come. Instead he lay there wallowing now in the seas and the old man pulled the skiff up to him.

When he was even with him and had the fish's head against the bow he could not believe his size. But he untied the harpoon rope from the bitt, passed it through the fish's gills and out his jaws, made a turn around his sword then passed the rope through the other gill, made another turn around the bill and knotted the double rope and made it fast to the bitt in the bow. He cut the rope then and went astern to noose the tail. The fish had turned silver from his original purple and silver, and the stripes showed the same pale violet colour as his tail. They were wider than a man's hand with his fingers spread and the fish's eye looked as detached as the mirrors in a periscope or as a saint in a procession.

"It was the only way to kill him," the old man said. He was feeling better since the water and he knew he would not go away and his head was clear. He's over fifteen hundred pounds the way he is, he thought. Maybe much more. If he dresses out two-thirds of that at thirty cents a pound?

---

1 **to splice:** spleißen, splissen.
4 **to wallow:** sich wälzen.
6 **to be even with s.o.:** auf gleicher Höhe mit jdm. sein.
8 **to untie:** losbinden, lösen.
13 **to noose:** an-, festschlingen.
15 **violet:** violett.
17 f. **detached:** unbeteiligt, regungslos.
18 **periscope:** Periskop, Sehrohr.

80

"I need a pencil for that," he said. "My head is not that clear. But I think the great DiMaggio would be proud of me today. I had no bone spurs. But the hands and the back hurt truly." I wonder what a bone spur is,
5 he thought. Maybe we have them without knowing of it.

He made the fish fast to bow and stern and to the middle thwart. He was so big it was like lashing a much bigger skiff alongside. He cut a piece of line and tied
10 the fish's lower jaw against his bill so his mouth would not open and they would sail as cleanly as possible. Then he stepped the mast and, with the stick that was his gaff and with his boom rigged, the patched sail drew, the boat began to move, and half lying in the
15 stern he sailed south-west.

He did not need a compass to tell him where south-west was. He only needed the feel of the trade wind and the drawing of the sail. I better put a small line out with a spoon on it and try and get something to eat and
20 drink for the moisture. But he could not find a spoon and his sardines were rotten. So he hooked a patch of yellow Gulf weed with the gaff as they passed and shook it so that the small shrimps that were in it fell on to the planking of the skiff. There were more than a
25 dozen of them and they jumped and kicked like sand fleas. The old man pinched their heads off with his thumb and forefinger and ate them chewing up the

---

13 **boom:** Baum, Spiere (Stange der Takelage).
14 **to draw:** sich füllen (Segel).
19 **spoon:** Blinker (blinkender Metallköder).
20 **moisture:** Feuchtigkeit.
25 f. **sand flea:** Sandfloh.

shells and the tails. They were very tiny but he knew they were nourishing and they tasted good.

The old man still had two drinks of water in the bottle and he used half of one after he had eaten the shrimps. The skiff was sailing well considering the handicaps and he steered with the tiller under his arm. He could see the fish and he had only to look at his hands and feel his back against the stern to know that this had truly happened and was not a dream. At one time when he was feeling so badly toward the end, he had thought perhaps it was a dream. Then when he had seen the fish come out of the water and hang motionless in the sky before he fell, he was sure there was some great strangeness and he could not believe it. Then he could not see well, although now he saw as well as ever.

Now he knew there was the fish and his hands and back were no dream. The hands cure quickly, he thought. I bled them clean and the salt water will heal them. The dark water of the true gulf is the greatest healer that there is. All I must do is keep the head clear. The hands have done their work and we sail well. With his mouth shut and his tail straight up and down we sail like brothers. Then his head started to become a little unclear and he thought, is he bringing me in or am I bringing him in? If I were towing him behind there would be no question. Nor if the fish were in the skiff, with all dignity gone, there would be no question either. But they were sailing together lashed side by side and the old man thought, let him bring me in if it

---

6 **tiller:** Ruderpinne.
18 **to bleed s.th. clean:** etwas ausbluten lassen.
20 **healer:** Heilmittel.

pleases him. I am only better than him through trickery and he meant me no harm.

They sailed well and the old man soaked his hands in the salt water and tried to keep his head clear. There were high cumulus clouds and enough cirrus above them so that the old man knew the breeze would last all night. The old man looked at the fish constantly to make sure it was true. It was an hour before the first shark hit him.

The shark was not an accident. He had come up from deep down in the water as the dark cloud of blood had settled and dispersed in the mile-deep sea. He had come up so fast and absolutely without caution that he broke the surface of the blue water and was in the sun. Then he fell back into the sea and picked up the scent and started swimming on the course the skiff and the fish had taken.

Sometimes he lost the scent. But he would pick it up again, or have just a trace of it, and he swam fast and hard on the course. He was a very big Mako shark built to swim as fast as the fastest fish in the sea and everything about him was beautiful except his jaws. His back was as blue as a swordfish's and his belly was silver and his hide was smooth and handsome. He was built as a swordfish except for his huge jaws which were tight shut now as he swam fast, just under the surface with his high dorsal fin knifing through the water without

---

1 **trickery:** Kniffe, Listen, Schliche.
3 **to soak:** einweichen.
12 **to disperse:** sich verteilen.
20 **Mako shark:** Makohai.
23 **swordfish:** Schwertfisch.
27 **to knife:** (durch)schneiden.

wavering. Inside the closed double lip of his jaws all of his eight rows of teeth were slanted inwards. They were not the ordinary pyramid-shaped teeth of most sharks. They were shaped like a man's fingers when they are
5 crisped like claws. They were nearly as long as the fingers of the old man and they had razor-sharp cutting edges on both sides. This was a fish built to feed on all the fishes in the sea, that were so fast and strong and well armed that they had no other enemy. Now he
10 speeded up as he smelled the fresher scent and his blue dorsal fin cut the water.

When the old man saw him coming he knew that this was a shark that had no fear at all and would do exactly what he wished. He prepared the harpoon and made
15 the rope fast while he watched the shark come on. The rope was short as it lacked what he had cut away to lash the fish.

The old man's head was clear and good now and he was full of resolution but he had little hope. It was too
20 good to last, he thought. He took one look at the great fish as he watched the shark close in. It might as well have been a dream, he thought. I cannot keep him from hitting me but maybe I can get him. *Dentuso*, he thought. Bad luck to your mother.
25 The shark closed fast astern and when he hit the fish

---

1 **to waver:** zaudern, zögern.
3 **pyramid-shaped:** pyramidenförmig.
5 **to crisp:** hier: sich zusammenkrallen.
6 **razor-sharp:** rasiermesserscharf.
6 f. **cutting edge:** Schnittkante.
21 **to close in** (auch: *to close*): heranrücken, näher kommen, sich nähern.
23 **dentuso** (Span.): Hai(fisch) (wörtl.: scharfzahnig).

the old man saw his mouth open and his strange eyes
and the clicking chop of the teeth as he drove forward
in the meat just above the tail. The shark's head was
out of water and his back was coming out and the old
man could hear the noise of skin and flesh ripping on
the big fish when he rammed the harpoon down onto
the shark's head at a spot where the line between his
eyes intersected with the line that ran straight back
from his nose. There were no such lines. There was
only the heavy sharp blue head and the big eyes and
the clicking, thrusting, all-swallowing jaws. But that
was the location of the brain and the old man hit it. He
hit it with his blood-mushed hands driving a good harpoon with all his strength. He hit it without hope but
with resolution and complete malignancy.

The shark swung over and the old man saw his eye
was not alive and then he swung over once again, wrap-
ping himself in two loops of the rope. The old man
knew that he was dead but the shark would not accept
it. Then, on his back, with his tail lashing and his jaws
clicking, the shark ploughed over the water as a speed-
boat does. The water was white where his tail beat it
and three-quarters of his body was clear above the wa-

---

2 **to click:** klacken, klicken, knacken.
  chop: Zuschnappen.
  to drive forward: vorstoßen.
5 **to rip:** zerreißen.
6 **to ram:** rammen.
8 **to intersect:** sich kreuzen.
11 **to thrust:** anfallen, zustoßen.
13 **blood-mushed:** blutig gequetscht.
15 **malignancy:** Bösartigkeit, Bosheit, Feindseligkeit.
21 f. **speed-boat:** Schnell-, Rennboot.

ter when the rope came taut, shivered, and then snapped. The shark lay quietly for a little while on the surface and the old man watched him. Then he went down very slowly.

5 "He took about forty pounds," the old man said aloud. He took my harpoon too and all the rope, he thought, and now my fish bleeds again and there will be others.

He did not like to look at the fish any more since he 10 had been mutilated. When the fish had been hit it was as though he himself were hit.

But I killed the shark that hit my fish, he thought. And he was the biggest *dentuso* that I have ever seen. And God knows that I have seen big ones.

15 It was too good to last, he thought. I wish it had been a dream now and that I had never hooked the fish and was alone in bed on the newspapers.

"But man is not made for defeat," he said. "A man can be destroyed but not defeated." I am sorry that I 20 killed the fish though, he thought. Now the bad time is coming and I do not even have the harpoon. The *dentuso* is cruel and able and strong and intelligent. But I was more intelligent than he was. Perhaps not, he thought. Perhaps I was only better armed.

25 "Don't think, old man," he said aloud. "Sail on this course and take it when it comes."

But I must think, he thought. Because it is all I have left. That and baseball. I wonder how the great DiMaggio would have like the way I hit him in the brain. It 30 was no great thing, he thought. Any man could do it.

---

2 **to snap:** (zer)reißen.
10 **to mutilate:** verstümmeln.

But do you think my hands were as great a handicap as the bone spurs? I cannot know. I never had anything wrong with my heel except the time the sting ray stung it when I stepped on him when swimming and para-
5 lysed the lower leg and made the unbearable pain.

"Think about something cheerful, old man," he said. "Every minute now you are closer to home. You sail lighter for the loss of forty pounds."

He knew quite well the pattern of what could happen
10 when he reached the inner part of the current. But there was nothing to be done now.

"Yes there is," he said aloud. "I can lash my knife to the butt of one of the oars."

So he did that with the tiller under his arm and the
15 sheet of the sail under his foot.

"Now," he said. "I am still an old man. But I am not unarmed."

The breeze was fresh now and he sailed on well. He watched only the forward part of the fish and some of
20 his hope returned.

It is silly not to hope, he thought. Besides I believe it is a sin. Do not think about sin, he thought. There are enough problems now without sin. Also I have no un-derstanding of it.
25 I have no unterstanding of it and I am not sure that I believe in it. Perhaps it was a sin to kill the fish. I sup-

---

3 **sting ray:** Stechrochen.
4 f. **to paralyse:** paralysieren, lähmen.
5 **unbearable:** unerträglich.
13 **butt:** (dickes, unteres) Ende.
15 **sheet:** Schot(e) (Tau, das ein Segel in die richtige Stellung zum Wind bringt).

pose it was even though I did it to keep me alive and
feed many people. But then everything is a sin. Do not
think about sin. It is much too late for that and there
are people who are paid to do it. Let them think about
it. You were born to be a fisherman as the fish was born
to be a fish. San Pedro was a fisherman as was the father of the great DiMaggio.

But he liked to think about all things that he was in-
volved in and since there was nothing to read and he
did not have a radio, he thought much and he kept
on thinking about sin. You did not kill the fish only
to keep alive and to sell for food, he thought. You
killed him for pride and because you are a fisherman.
You loved him when he was alive and you loved him
after. If you love him, it is not a sin to kill him. Or is it
more?

"You think too much, old man," he said aloud.

But you enjoyed killing the *dentuso*, he thought. He
lives on the live fish as you do. He is not a scavenger
nor just a moving appetite as some sharks are. He is
beautiful and noble and knows no fear of anything.

"I killed him in self-defence," the old man said
aloud. "And I killed him well."

Besides, he thought, everything kills everything else
in some way. Fishing kills me exactly as it keeps me
alive. The boy keeps me alive, he thought. I must not
deceive myself too much.

He leaned over the side and pulled loose a piece of
the meat of the fish where the shark had cut him. He
chewed it and noted its quality and its good taste. It

6 **San Pedro:** hl. Petrus (Schutzpatron der Fischer).
19 **scavenger:** Aasfresser.

was firm and juicy, like meat, but it was not red. There was no stringiness in it and he knew that it would bring the highest price in the market. But there was no way to keep its scent out of the water and the old man knew that a very bad time was coming.

The breeze was steady. It had backed a little further into the north-east and he knew that meant that it would not fall off. The old man looked ahead of him but he could see no sails nor could he see the hull nor the smoke of any ship. There were only the flying fish that went up from his bow sailing away to either side and the yellow patches of Gulf weed. He could not even see a bird.

He had sailed for two hours, resting in the stern and sometimes chewing a bit of the meat from the marlin, trying to rest and to be strong, when he saw the first of the two sharks.

"Ay," he said aloud. There is no translation for this word and perhaps it is just a noise such as a man might make, involuntarily, feeling the nail go through his hands and into the wood.

"Galanos," he said aloud. He had seen the second fin now coming up behind the first and had identified them as shovel-nosed sharks by the brown, triangular fin and the sweeping movements of the tail. They had the scent

---

2 **stringiness:** Zähigkeit.
8 **to fall off:** abflauen.
9 **hull:** (Schiffs-)Rumpf.
18 **ay** (Span.): au(tsch).
20 **involuntarily** (adv.): unfreiwillig, unwillkürlich.
22 **galano** (Span.): Schaufelhai.
24 **shovel-nosed:** schaufelnasig.
   triangular: dreieckig.

and were excited and in the stupidity of their great hunger they were losing and finding the scent in their excitement. But they were closing all the time.

The old man made the sheet fast and jammed the tiller. Then he took up the oar with the knife lashed to it. He lifted it as lightly as he could because his hands rebelled at the pain. Then he opened and closed them on it lightly to loosen them. He closed them firmly so they would take the pain now and would not flinch and watched the sharks come. He could see their wide, flattened, shovel-pointed heads now and their white-tipped wide pectoral fins. They were hateful sharks, bad-smelling, scavengers as well as killers, and when they were hungry they would bite at an oar or the rudder of a boat. It was these sharks that would cut the turtles' legs and flippers off when the turtles were asleep on the surface, and they would hit a man in the water, if they were hungry, even if the man had no smell of fish blood nor of fish slime on him.

"*Ay,*" the old man said. "*Galanos.* Come on, *Galanos.*"

They came. But they did not come as the Mako had come. One turned and went out of sight under the skiff and the old man could feel the skiff shake as he jerked

---

1 **stupidity:** Dummheit.
6 f. **to rebel at s.th.:** gegen etwas rebellieren, aufbegehren, sich gegen etwas auflehnen.
9 **to flinch:** zusammenfahren, -zucken.
11 f. **white-tipped:** mit weißer Spitze.
12 **hateful:** abscheulich, widerlich.
14 f. **rudder:** (Steuer-)Ruder.
16 **flipper:** Paddel (Seeschildkröte).
19 **slime:** Glibber, Schleim.

and pulled on the fish. The other watched the old man
with his slitted yellow eyes and then came in fast with
his half circle of jaws wide to hit the fish where he had
already been bitten. The line showed clearly on the top
5 of his brown head and back where the brain joined the
spinal cord and the old man drove the knife on the oar
into the juncture, withdrew it, and drove it in again into
the shark's yellow cat-like eyes. The shark let go of the
fish and slid down, swallowing what he had taken as he
10 died.

The skiff was still shaking with the destruction the
other shark was doing to the fish and the old man let go
the sheet so that the skiff would swing broadside and
bring the shark out from under. When he saw the shark
15 he leaned over the side and punched at him. He hit
only meat and the hide was set hard and he barely got
the knife in. The blow hurt not only his hands but his
shoulder too. But the shark came up fast with his head
out and the old man hit him squarely in the centre of
20 his flat-topped head as his nose came out of the water
and lay against the fish. The old man withdrew the
blade and punched the shark exactly in the same spot
again. He still hung to the fish with his jaws locked and
the old man stabbed him in his left eye. The shark still
25 hung there.

"No?" the old man said and he drove the blade be-

---

2 **slitted eye:** Schlitzauge.
6 **spinal cord:** Rückenmark.
7 **juncture:** Naht, Verbindungsstelle.
13 **broadside** (adv.): breitseitig, zur Breitseite.
19 **squarely** (adv.): direkt.
20 **flat-topped:** abgeflacht.
24 **to stab:** stechen.

tween the vertebrae and the brain. It was an easy shot now and he felt the cartilage sever. The old man reversed the oar and put the blade between the shark's jaws to open them. He twisted the blade and as the shark slid loose he said, "Go on, *galano*. Slide down a mile deep. Go and see your friend, or maybe it's your mother."

The old man wiped the blade of his knife and laid down the oar. Then he found the sheet and the sail filled and he brought the skiff on to her course.

"They must have taken a quarter of him and of the best meat," he said aloud. "I wish it were a dream and that I had never hooked him. I'm sorry about it, fish. It makes everything wrong." He stopped and he did not want to look at the fish now. Drained of blood and awash he looked the colour of the silver backing of a mirror and his stripes still showed.

"I shouldn't have gone out so far, fish," he said. "Neither for you nor for me. I'm sorry, fish."

Now, he said to himself. Look to the lashing on the knife and see if it has been cut. Then get your hand in order because there still is more to come.

"I wish I had a stone for the knife," the old man said after he had checked the lashing on the oar butt. "I should have brought a stone." You should have brought many things, he thought. But you did not bring them, old man. Now is no time to think of what you do not have. Think of what you can do with what there is.

---

1 **vertebrae** (pl.): Rückgrat, Wirbel(säule).
2 **cartilage:** Knorpel.
16 **awash:** unter Wasser.

"You give me much good counsel," he said aloud.
"I'm tired of it."

He held the tiller under his arm and soaked both his
hands in the water as the skiff drove forward.

5   "God knows how much that last one took," he said.
"But she's much lighter now." He did not want to think
of the mutilated under-side of the fish. He knew that
each of the jerking bumps of the shark had been meat
torn away and that the fish now made a trail for all
10 sharks as wide as a highway through the sea.

He was a fish to keep a man all winter, he thought.
Don't think of that. Just rest and try to get your hands
in shape to defend what is left of him. The blood smell
from my hands means nothing now with all that scent
15 in the water. Besides they do not bleed much. There is
nothing cut that means anything. The bleeding may
keep the left from cramping.

What can I think of now? he thought. Nothing. I
must think of nothing and wait for the next ones. I wish
20 it had really been a dream, he thought. But who
knows? It might have turned out well.

The next shark that came was a single shovel-nose.
He came like a pig to the trough if a pig had a mouth
so wide that you could put your head in it. The old man
25 let him hit the fish and then drove the knife on the oar
down into his brain. But the shark jerked backwards as
he rolled and the knife blade snapped.

The old man settled himself to steer. He did not even

---

 1 **counsel:** Rat(schlag).
 8 **bump:** Stoß.
22 **shovel-nose:** Schaufelhai.
23 **trough:** Trog.

watch the big shark sinking slowly in the water, showing first life-size, then small, then tiny. That always fascinated the old man. But he did not even watch it now.

"I have the gaff now," he said. "But it will do no
5 good. I have the two oars and the tiller and the short club."

Now they have beaten me, he thought. I am too old to club sharks to death. But I will try it as long as I have the oars and the short club and the tiller.

10 He put his hands in the water again to soak them. It was getting late in the afternoon and he saw nothing but the sea and the sky. There was more wind in the sky than there had been, and soon he hoped that he would see land.

15 "You're tired, old man," he said. "You're tired inside."

The sharks did not hit him again until just before sunset.

The old man saw the brown fins coming along the
20 wide trail the fish must make in the water. They were not even quartering on the scent. They were headed straight for the skiff swimming side by side.

He jammed the tiller, made the sheet fast and reached under the stern for the club. It was an oar
25 handle from a broken oar sawed off to about two and a half feet in length. He could only use it effectively with one hand because of the grip of the handle and he took good hold of it with his right hand, flexing his hand on it, as he watched the sharks come. They were
30 both *galanos*.

---

2 f. **to fascinate:** faszinieren, in Bann schlagen.
21 **to quarter:** umherschweifen, -schwimmen.
28 **to flex:** anspannen, beugen, biegen.

I must let the first one get a good hold and hit him on the point of the nose or straight across the top of the head, he thought.

The two sharks closed together and as he saw the one nearest him open his jaws and sink them into the silver side of the fish, he raised the club high and brought it down heavy and slamming on to the top of the shark's broad head. He felt the rubbery solidity as the club came down. But he felt the rigidity of bone too and he struck the shark once more hard across the point of the nose as he slid down from the fish.

The other shark had been in and out and now came in again with his jaws wide. The old man could see pieces of the meat of the fish spilling white from the corner of his jaws as he bumped the fish and closed his jaws. He swung at him and hit only the head and the shark looked at him and wrenched the meat loose. The old man swung the club down on him again as he slipped away to swallow and hit only the heavy solid rubberiness.

"Come on, *galano*," the old man said. "Come in again."

The shark came in in a rush and the old man hit him as he shut his jaws. He hit him solidly and from as high up as he could raise the club.This time he felt the bone at the base of the brain and he hit him again in the

---

5 **to sink one's jaws into s.th.:** die Zähne in etwas schlagen.
7 **to slam:** knallen, krachen, schlagen.
8 **rubbery:** gummiartig, elastisch.
  solidity: Festigkeit.
9 **rigidity:** Härte, Starre, Steifheit.
14 **to spill:** hervorquellen; hier: heraushängen.
17 **to wrench loose:** losfetzen, -reißen, -zerren.
20 **rubberiness:** Gummiartigkeit.

same place while the shark tore the meat loose sluggishly and slid down from the fish.

The old man watched for him to come again but neither shark showed. Then he saw one on the surface swimming in circles. He did not see the fin of the other.

I could not expect to kill them, he thought. I could have in my time. But I have hurt them both badly and neither one can feel very good. If I could have used a bat with two hands I could have killed the first one surely. Even now, he thought.

He did not want to look at the fish. He knew that half of him had been destroyed. The sun had gone down while he had been in the fight with the sharks.

"It will be dark soon," he said. "Then I should see the glow of Havana. If I am too far to the eastward I will see the lights of one of the new beaches."

I cannot be too far out now, he thought. I hope no one has been too worried. There is only the boy to worry, of course. But I am sure he would have confidence. Many of the older fishermen will worry. Many others too, he thought. I live in a good town.

He could not talk to the fish any more because the fish had been ruined too badly. Then something came into his head.

"Half-fish," he said. "Fish that you were. I am sorry that I went too far out. I ruined us both. But we have killed many sharks, you and I, and ruined many others. How many did you ever kill, old fish? You do not have that spear on your head for nothing."

He liked to think of the fish and what he could do to a shark if he were swimming free. I should have

---

1 f. **sluggishly** (adv.): träge, langsam, schwerfällig.

chopped the bill off to fight them with, he thought. But
there was no hatchet and then there was no knife.

But if I had, and could have lashed it to an oar butt,
what a weapon. Then we might have fought them to-
5 gether. What will you do now if they come in the night?
What can you do?

"Fight them," he said. "I'll fight them until I die."

But in the dark now and no glow showing and no
lights and only the wind and the steady pull of the sail
10 he felt that perhaps he was already dead. He put his
two hands together and felt the palms. They were not
dead and he could bring the pain of life by simply
opening and closing them. He leaned his back against
the stern and knew he was not dead. His shoulders told
15 him.

I have all those prayers I promised if I caught the
fish, he thought. But I am too tired to say them now. I
better get the sack and put it over my shoulders.

He lay in the stern and steered and watched for the
20 glow to come in the sky. I have half of him, he thought.
Maybe I'll have the luck to bring the forward half in. I
should have some luck. No, he said. You violated your
luck when you went too far outside.

"Don't be silly," he said aloud. "And keep awake and
25 steer. You may have much luck yet.

I'd like to buy some if there's any place they sell it,"
he said.

What could I buy it with? he asked himself. Could I
buy it with a lost harpoon and a broken knife and two
30 bad hands?

---

2 **hatchet:** Beil.
22 f. **to violate one's luck:** sein Glück aufs Spiel setzen.

"You might," he said. "You tried to buy it with eighty-four days at sea. They nearly sold it to you too."

I must not think nonsense, he thought. Luck is a thing that comes in many forms and who can recognize her? I would take some though in any form and pay what they asked. I wish I could see the glow from the lights, he thought. I wish too many things. But that is the thing I wish for now. He tried to settle more comfortably to steer and from his pain he knew he was not dead.

He saw the reflected glare of the lights of the city at what must have been around ten o'clock at night. They were only perceptible at first as the light is in the sky before the moon rises. Then they were steady to see across the ocean which was rough now with the increasing breeze. He steered inside of the glow and he thought that now, soon, he must hit the edge of the stream.

Now it is over, he thought. They will probably hit me again. But what can a man do against them in the dark without a weapon?

He was stiff and sore now and his wounds and all of the strained parts of his body hurt with the cold of the night. I hope I do not have to fight again, he thought. I hope so much I do not have to fight again.

But by midnight he fought and this time he knew the fight was useless. They came in a pack and he could only see the lines in the water that their fins made and their phosphorescence as they threw themselves on the fish. He clubbed at heads and heard the jaws chop and the shaking of the skiff as they took hold below. He

13 **perceptible:** wahrnehmbar, zu erkennen.

clubbed desperately at what he could only feel and hear and he felt something seize the club and it was gone.

He jerked the tiller free from the rudder and beat and chopped with it, holding it in both hands and driving it down again and again. But they were up to the bow now and driving in one after the other and together, tearing off the pieces of meat that showed glowing below the sea as they turned to come once more.

One came, finally, against the head itself and he knew that it was over. He swung the tiller across the shark's head where the jaws were caught in the heaviness of the fish's head which would not tear. He swung it once and twice and again. He heard the tiller break and he lunged at the shark with the splintered butt. He felt it go in and knowing it was sharp he drove it in again. The shark let go and rolled away. That was the last shark of the pack that came. There was nothing more for them to eat.

The old man could hardly breathe now and he felt a strange taste in his mouth. It was coppery and sweet and he was afraid of it for a moment. But there was not much of it.

He spat into the ocean and said, "Eat that, *galanos*. And make a dream you've killed a man."

He knew he was beaten now finally and without remedy and he went back to the stern and found the jagged

---

15 **to lunge:** stoßen.
   to splinter: zersplittern.
21 **coppery:** kupferartig, kupferig.
26 f. **without remedy:** rettungslos.
27 **jagged:** ausgezackt.

end of the tiller would fit in the slot of the rudder well enough for him to steer. He settled the sack around his shoulders and put the skiff on her course. He sailed lightly now and he had no thoughts nor any feelings of any kind. He was past everything now and he sailed the skiff to make his home port as well and as intelligently as he could. In the night sharks hit the carcass as someone might pick up crumbs from the table. The old man paid no attention to them and did not pay any attention to anything except steering. He only noticed how lightly and how well the skiff sailed now there was no great weight beside her.

She's good, he thought. She is sound and not harmed in any way except for the tiller. That is easily replaced.

He could feel he was inside the current now and he could see the lights of the beach colonies along the shore. He knew where he was now and it was nothing to get home.

The wind is our friend, anyway, he thought. Then he added, sometimes. And the great sea with our friends and our enemies. And bed, he thought. Bed is my friend. Just bed, he thought. Bed will be a great thing. It is easy when you are beaten, he thought. I never knew how easy it was. And what beat you, he thought.

"Nothing," he said aloud. "I went out too far."

When he sailed into the little harbour the lights of the Terrace were out and he knew everyone was in bed. The breeze had risen steadily and was blowing strongly now. It was quiet in the harbour though and he sailed

---

1 **slot:** Kerbe, Schlitz.
6 **to make one's home port:** den Heimathafen anlaufen.
8 **crumb:** Brosame, Krume, Krümel.

up onto the little patch of shingle below the rocks. There was no one to help him so he pulled the boat up as far as he could. Then he stepped out and made her fast to a rock.

5 He unstepped the mast and furled the sail and tied it. Then he shouldered the mast and started to climb. It was then he knew the depth of his tiredness. He stopped for a moment and looked back and saw in the reflection from the street light the great tail of the fish
10 standing up well behind the skiff's stern. He saw the white naked line of his backbone and the dark mass of the head with the projecting bill and all the nakedness between.

He started to climb again and at the top he fell and
15 lay for some time with the mast across his shoulder. He tried to get up. But it was too difficult and he sat there with the mast on his shoulder and looked at the road. A cat passed on the far side going about its business and the old man watched it. Then he just watched the
20 road.

Finally he put the mast down and stood up. He picked the mast up and put it on his shoulder and started up the road. He had to sit down five times before he reached his shack.

25 Inside the shack he leaned the mast against the wall. In the dark he found a water bottle and took a drink. Then he lay down on the bed. He pulled the blanket over his shoulders and then over his back and legs and he slept face down on the newspapers with his arms out
30 straight and the palms of his hands up.

---

1 **shingle:** Kies(strand).

He was asleep when the boy looked in the door in the morning. It was blowing so hard that the drifting boats would not be going out and the boy had slept late and then come to the old man's shack as he had come
5 each morning. The boy saw the old man was breathing and then he saw the old man's hands and he started to cry. He went out very quietly to go to bring some coffee and all the way down the road he was crying.

Many fishermen were around the skiff looking at
10 what was lashed beside it and one was in the water, his trousers rolled up, measuring the skeleton with a length of line.

The boy did not go down. He had been there before and one of the fishermen was looking after the skiff for
15 him.

"How is he?" one of the fishermen shouted.

"Sleeping," the boy called. He did not care that they saw him crying. "Let no one disturb him."

"He was eighteen feet from nose to tail," the fisher-
20 man who was measuring him called.

"I believe it," the boy said.

He went into the Terrace and asked for a can of coffee.

"Hot and with plenty of milk and sugar in it."

25 "Anything more?"

"No. Afterwards I will see what he can eat."

"What a fish it was," the proprietor said. "There has never been such a fish. Those were two fine fish you took yesterday too."

30 "Damn my fish," the boy said and he started to cry again.

---

11 **skeleton:** Skelett, Gerippe.

"Do you want a drink of any kind?" the proprietor asked.

"No," the boy said. "Tell them not to bother Santiago. I'll be back."

"Tell him how sorry I am."

"Thanks," the boy said.

The boy carried the hot can of coffee up to the old man's shack and sat by him until he woke. Once it looked as though he were waking. But he had gone back into heavy sleep and the boy had gone across the road to borrow some wood to heat the coffee.

Finally the old man woke.

"Don't sit up," the boy said. "Drink this." He poured some of the coffee in a glass.

The old man took it and drank it.

"They beat me, Manolin," he said. "They truly beat me."

"*He* didn't beat you. Not the fish."

"No. Truly. It was afterwards."

"Pedrico is looking after the skiff and the gear. What do you want done with the head?"

"Let Pedrico chop it up to use in fish traps."

"And the spear?"

"You keep it if you want it."

"I want it," the boy said. "Now we must make our plans about the other things."

"Did they search for me?"

"Of course. With coast guard and with planes."

"The ocean is very big and a skiff is small and hard to see," the old man said. He noticed how pleasant it was to have someone to talk to instead of speaking only to himself and to the sea. "I missed you," he said. "What did you catch?"

"One the first day. One the second and two the third."

"Very good."

"Now we fish together again."

"No. I am not lucky. I am not lucky any more."

"The hell with luck," the boy said, "I'll bring the luck with me."

"What will your family say?"

"I do not care. I caught two yesterday. But we will fish together now for I still have much to learn."

"We must get a good killing lance and always have it on board. You can make the blade from a spring leaf from an old Ford. We can grind it in Guanabacoa. It should be sharp and not tempered so it will break. My knife broke."

"I'll get another knife and have the spring ground. How many days of heavy *brisa* have we?"

"Maybe three. Maybe more."

"I will have everything in order," the boy said. "You get your hands well, old man."

"I know how to care for them. In the night I spat something strange and felt something in my chest was broken."

"Get that well too," the boy said. "Lie down, old man, and I will bring you your clean shirt. And something to eat."

"Bring any of the papers of the time that I was gone," the old man said.

"You must get well fast for there is much that I can

---

11 **killing lance:** Fischspeer.
13 **Guanabacoa:** Vorort von Havanna.

learn and you can teach me everything. How much did you suffer?"

"Plenty," the old man said.

"I'll bring the food and the papers," the boy said. "Rest well, old man. I will bring stuff from the drugstore for your hands."

"Don't forget to tell Pedrico the head is his."

"No. I will remember."

As the boy went out the door and down the worn coral rock road he was crying again.

That afternoon there was a party of tourists at the Terrace and looking down in the water among the empty beer cans and dead barracudas a woman saw a great long white spine with a huge tail at the end that lifted and swung with the tide while the east wind blew a heavy steady sea outside the entrance to the harbour.

"What's that?" she asked a waiter and pointed to the long backbone of the great fish that was now just garbage waiting to go out with the tide.

"Tiburon," the waiter said. "Eshark." He was meaning to explain what had happened.

"I didn't know sharks had such handsome, beautifully formed tails."

"I didn't either," her male companion said.

Up the road, in his shack, the old man was sleeping again. He was still sleeping on his face and the boy was sitting by him watching him. The old man was dreaming about the lions.

---

13 **barracuda** (Span.): Barracuda, Pfeilhecht.
14 **spine:** Rückgrat, Wirbelsäule.
20 **tiburon:** *tiburón* (Span.): Hai(fisch).
   eshark: *a shark.*

Editorische Notiz

Der englische Text folgt der Ausgabe: Ernest Hemingway, *The Old Man and the Sea*, London: Arrow Books, 1993. Das Glossar erklärt in der Regel alle Wörter und Redewendungen, die nicht in *Reclams Englischem Wörterbuch* von Dieter Hamblock (Stuttgart: Reclam, 1996) verzeichnet sind.

Im Glossar verwendete Abkürzungen

adv.	adverb
Am. Span.	American Spanish
arch.	archaic (altertümlich)
coll.	colloquial (umgangssprachlich)
fig.	figuratively (übertragen)
Lat.	Latin
o.s.	oneself
pl.	plural
Span./span.	Spanish/spanisch
s.o.	someone
s.th.	something

Literaturhinweise

I. *Werke*

Three Stories and Ten Poems, Paris: Contact Publishing Company, 1923.

In Our Time, Paris: Three Mountains Press, 1924. [Limitierte Auflage.] Erweiterte Ausgabe: New York: Boni & Liveright, 1925.

The Torrents of Spring. A Romantic Novel in Honor of the Passing of a Great Race, New York: Scribner, 1926.

The Sun Also Rises, New York: Scribner, 1926. [In Großbritannien u. d. T. *Fiesta*.]

Men Without Women, New York: Scribner, 1927.

A Farewell to Arms, New York: Scribner, 1929.

Death in the Afternoon, New York: Scribner, 1932.

Winner Take Nothing, New York: Scribner, 1933.

Green Hills of Africa, New York: Scribner, 1935.

The Snows of Kilimanjaro, New York: Scribner, 1936.

To Have and Have Not, New York: Scribner, 1937.

The Fifth Column and The First Forty-nine Stories, New York: Scribner, 1938.

The Spanish War, London: Fact, 1938.

The Spanish Earth, Cleveland: J. B. Savage, 1938.

For Whom the Bell Tolls, New York: Scribner, 1940.

(Hrsg.) *Men at War. The Best War Stories of All Time. Based on a Plan by William Kozlenko*, New York: Crown Publishers, 1942.

The Portable Hemingway, hrsg. von Malcolm Cowley, New York: Viking Press, 1944.

The Essential Hemingway, London: Cape, 1947.

Across the River and Into the Trees, New York: Scribner, 1950.

Selected Stories, London: Cape, 1951.

The Old Man and the Sea, New York: Scribner, 1952.

The Hemingway Reader, hrsg. von Charles Poore, New York: Scribner, 1953.

The Collected Poems, New York: Seven Sirens Press, 1955 (The Library of Living Poets, 1).

The Wild Years, hrsg. von Gene Z. Hanrahan, New York: Dell, 1962.

A Moveable Feast, New York: Scribner, 1964.

By-Line: Ernest Hemingway. Selected Articles and Dispatches of Four Decades, hrsg. von William White, New York: Scribner, 1967.

Islands in the Stream, New York: Scribner, 1970.

The Fifth Column and Four Stories of the Spanish Civil War, New York: Bantam, 1970.

Ernest Hemingway. Cub Reporter. »Kansas City Star« Stories, hrsg. von Matthew J. Bruccoli, Pittsburgh: University of Pittsburgh Press, 1970.

Ernest Hemingway's Apprenticeship. Pak Park, 1916–1917, hrsg. von Matthew J. Bruccoli, Washington (D.C.): NCR Microcard Editions, 1971.

The Nick Adams Stories, New York: Scribner, 1972.

The Enduring Hemingway. An Anthology of a Lifetime in Literature, hrsg. von Charles Scribner, New York: Scribner, 1974.

88 Poems, hrsg. von Nicholas Gerogiannis, New York / London: Harcourt Brace Jovanovich / Bruccoli Clark, 1979. Neuausgabe u. d. T. *The Complete Poems*, Omaha: University of Nebraska Press, 1992.

Selected Letters 1917–1961, hrsg. von Carlos Baker, New York: Scribner, 1981.

Hemingway on Writing, hrsg. von Larry W. Phillips, London: Granada, 1984.

The Dangerous Summer, New York: Scribner, 1985.

Dateline: Toronto, hrsg. von William White, New York: Scribner, 1985.

The Garden of Eden, New York: Scribner, 1986.

Short Stories, hrsg. von David Hughes, London: The Folio Society, 1986.

The Complete Short Stories, New York: Scribner, 1987.

The Collected Stories, hrsg. von James Fenton, London: David Campbell, 1995.

Only Thing That Counts. The Ernest Hemingway – Maxwell Perkins Correspondence 1925–1947, hrsg. von Matthew J. Bruccoli, Columbia (S. C.): University of South Carolina Press, 1996.

True at First Light. A Fictional Memoir, hrsg. von Patrick Hemingway, New York: Scribner, 1999.

II. *Sekundärliteratur*

Allen, Joseph, *For Whom the Bell Tolls. Ernest Hemingway's Undiscovered Country*, New York: Twayne, 1994.

Aronowitz, Alfred G. / Hamill, Peter, *Ernest Hemingway. The Life and Death of a Man*, New York: Lancer Books, 1961.

Asselineau, Roger, *The Literary Reputation of Hemingway in Europe*, New York: New York University Press, 1965.

Astre, Georges-Albert, *Ernest Hemingway in Selbstzeugnissen und Bilddokumenten*, Reinbek: Rowohlt, 1963 (rowohlts monographien, 73).

Atkins, John Alfred, *The Art of Ernest Hemingway. His Work and Personality*, London: P. Nevill, 1952.

Baden, Hans Jürgen, *Literatur und Selbstmord. Cesare Pavese, Klaus Mann und Ernest Hemingway*, Stuttgart: Klett, 1965.

Baker, Carlos (Hrsg.), *Ernest Hemingway. Critiques of Four Major Novels,* New York: Scribner, 1962.

– (Hrsg.), *Hemingway and His Critics. An International Anthology*, New York: Hill and Wang, 1961.

– *Ernest Hemingway. A Life Story*, New York: Scribner, 1969.

– *Hemingway. The Writer as Artist*, Princeton (N.J.): Princeton University Press, 1952.

Baker, Sheridan, *Hemingway. An Introduction and Interpretation*, New York: Holt, Rinehart and Winston, 1967.

Beegel, Susan F. (Hrsg.), *Hemingway's Neglected Short Fic-*

tion. New Perspectives, Birmingham: University of Alabama Press, 1989.

Benson, Jackson J. (Hrsg.), *New Critical Approaches to the Short Stories of Ernest Hemingway*, Durham (N.C.): Duke University Press, 1991.

– (Hrsg.), *The Short Stories of Ernest Hemingway. Critical Essays*, Durham (N.C.): Duke University Press, 1975.

– *Hemingway. The Writer's Art of Self-Defense*, Minneapolis: University of Minnesota Press, 1969.

Bloom, Harold, *Ernest Hemingway*, Broomall (Pa.): Chelsea House, 1990.

Brenner, Gerry, *Concealments in Hemingway's Work*, Columbus: Ohio State University Press, 1984.

– / Rovit, Earl, *Ernest Hemingway*, New York: Macmillan, 1986 (United States Authors Series, 497).

Brian, Denis (Hrsg.), *The True Gen. An Intimate Portrait of Ernest Hemingway by Those Who Knew Him*, New York: Grove Press, 1988.

Broer, Lawrence R., *Hemingway's Spanish Tragedy*, Birmingham: University of Alabama Press, 1973.

Bruccoli, Matthew J. (Hrsg.), *Conversations with Ernest Hemingway*, Jackson/London: University Press of Mississippi, 1986.

– *Fitzgerald and Hemingway. A Dangerous Friendship*, New York: Carroll & Graf, 1994.

– *Scott and Ernest. The Authority of Failure and the Authority of Success*, London: Bodley Head, 1978.

Burgess, Anthony, *Ernest Hemingway and His World*, New York: Scribner, 1978.

Burrill, William, *Hemingway. The Toronto Years*, New York: Doubleday, 1994.

Burwell, Rose Marie, *Hemingway. The Postwar Years and the Posthumous Novels*, Cambridge: Cambridge University Press, 1996.

Capellán, Angel, *Hemingway and the Hispanic World*, Ann Arbor (Mich.): University of Michigan Research Press, 1985 (Studies in Modern Literature, 51).

Carey, Gary, *Cliffs Notes on Hemingway's »The Old Man and the Sea«*, Lincoln (Neb.): Cliffs Notes, 1973.

Castillo-Puche, José Luis, *Hemingway in Spain. A Personal Reminiscence of Hemingway's Years in Spain by His Friend*, translated from the Spanish by Helen R. Lane, New York: Doubleday, 1984.

Clifford, Stephen P., *Beyond the Heroic »I«. Reading Lawrence, Hemingway, and »Masculinity«*, Lewisburg (Pa.): Bucknell University Press, 1998.

Comley, Nancy R. / Scholes, Robert, *Hemingway's Genders. Rereading the Hemingway Text*, New Haven / London: Yale University Press, 1994.

Conrad, Barnaby / Loomis, Dean, *Hemingway's Spain*, San Francisco: Chronicle Books, 1989.

Cooper, Stephen, *The Politics of Ernest Hemingway*, Ann Arbor (Mich.): University of Michigan Research Press, 1987 (Studies in Modern Literature, 71).

Dardis, Tom, *The Thirsty Muse. Alcohol and the American Writer*, New York: Ticknor & Fields, 1989.

DeFalco, Joseph, *The Hero in Hemingway's Short Stories*, Pittsburgh: University of Pittsburgh Press, 1963.

Dillon-Malone, Aubrey, *Hemingway. The Grace and the Pressure*, London: Robson, 1999.

Doctorow, E. L., *Jack London, Hemingway and the Constitution. Selected Essays 1977–1992*, New York: Random House, 1993.

Donaldson, Scott (Hrsg.), *The Cambridge Companion to Ernest Hemingway*, Cambridge: Cambridge University Press, 1996.

– *By Force of Will. The Life and Art of Hemingway*, New York: Viking Press, 1977.

– *Hemingway vs Fitzgerald. The Rise and Fall of a Literary Friendship*, London: John Murray, 2000.

Eby, Carl P., *Hemingway's Fetishism, Psychoanalysis and the Mirror of Manhood*, New York: State University of New York Press, 1999.

Fenton, Charles A., *The Apprenticeship of Ernest Heming-*

    way. The Early Years, New York: Farrar, Straus & Young, 1954.

Fleming, Robert E., *The Face in the Mirror. Hemingway's Writers*, Birmingham: University of Alabama Press, 1997.

Flora, Joseph M., *Ernest Hemingway. A Study of the Short Fiction*, New York: Twayne, 1989.

– *Hemingway's Nick Adams*, Baton Rouge: Louisiana State University Press, 1982.

Fuentes, Norberto, *Ernest Hemingway Rediscovered*, New York: Scribner, 1988.

– *Hemingway in Cuba*, Secancus (N.J.): Lyle Stuart, 1984.

Gaggin, John, *Hemingway and Nineteenth Century Aestheticism*, Ann Arbor (Mich.): University of Michigan Research Press, 1988 (Studies in Modern Literature, 91).

Goodwin, Donald W., *Alcohol and the Writer*, Harmondsworth: Penguin, 1988.

Graham, Kenneth, *York Notes on »The Old Man and the Sea«*, Harlow/Beirut: Longman / York Press, 1980.

Grebstein, Sheldon Norman, *Hemingway's Craft*, Carbondale: Southern Illinois University Press, 1973.

Griffin, Peter, *Along With Youth. Hemingway, The Early Years*, New York / Oxford: Oxford University Press, 1985.

– *Less Than A Treason. Hemingway in Paris*, New York / Oxford: Oxford University Press, 1990.

Grimes, Larry E., *The Religious Design of Hemingway's Early Fiction*, Ann Arbor (Mich.): University of Michigan Research Press, 1985 (Studies in Modern Literature, 50).

Gurko, Leo, *Hemingway and the Pursuit of Heroism*, New York: Crowell, 1968.

Hamod, Syed A., *The Short Fiction of Ernest Hemingway. A Study in Major Themes*, Springfield (Va.): Nataraj Books, 1985.

Hanneman, Audre, *Ernest Hemingway. A Comprehensive Bibliography*, Princeton (N.J.): Princeton University Press, 1967. Supplement: Princeton University Press, 1975.

Hardy, Richard E. / Cull, John G., *Hemingway. A Psychological Portrait*, New York: Irvington, 1987.

Harmon, Robert B., *Understanding Ernest Hermingway. A Study and Research Guide*, Metuchen (N.J.): Scarecrow Press, 1977.

Hemingway Sanford, Marcelline, *At the Hemingways. A Family Portrait*, Boston: Little Brown, 1962.

Hemingway, Gregory H., *Papa. A Personal Memoir*, Boston: Houghton Mifflin, 1976.

Hemingway, Leicester, *My Brother, Ernest Hemingway*, Cleveland: World Publishing, 1962.

Hemingway, Mary Welsh, *How It Was*, New York: Knopf, 1976.

Hotchner, A. E., *Hemingway and His World*, London: Viking, 1990.

– *Papa Hemingway. A Personal Memoir*, New York: Random House, 1966.

Hovey, Richard B., *Hemingway. The Inward Terrain*, Seattle: University of Washington Press, 1968.

Isabelle, Julanne, *Hemingway's Religious Experience*, New York: Vantage Press, 1964.

Jobes, Katharine T. (Hrsg.), *Twentieth Century Interpretations of »The Old Man and the Sea«. A Collection of Critical Essays*, Englewood Cliffs (N.J.): Prentice-Hall, 1968.

Johnston, Kenneth G., *The Tip of the Iceberg. Hemingway and the Short Story*, Greenwood (Fla.): Penkevill, 1987.

Kennedy, J. Gerald / Bryer, Jackson R., *French Connections. Hemingway and Fitzgerald Abroad*, New York: St. Martin's Press, 1998.

Kert, Bernice, *The Hemingway Women*. New York / London: Norton, 1983.

Kiley, Jed, *Hemingway. An Old Friend Remembers*, New York: Hawthorn Books, 1965.

Killinger, John, *Hemingway and the Dead Gods. A Study in Existentialism*, Lexington: University of Kentucky Press, 1960.

Kobler, Jasper F., *Ernest Hemingway. Journalist and Artist*, Ann Arbor (Mich.): University of Michigan Research Press, 1985 (Studies in Modern Literature, 44).

Kopp, Richard, *Ernest Hemingway: »Der alte Mann und das Meer«. Versuch einer Interpretation*, München: Oldenbourg, 1964.

Krotz, Friedrich Wilhelm, *Wesen und Funktion der Jagd im Werke Ernest Hemingways*, Diss. Freiburg i. Br. 1963.

Kvam, Wayne E., *Hemingway in Germany. The Fiction, the Legend, and the Critics*, Athens (Ohio): Ohio University Press, 1973.

Lania, Leo, *Hemingway. Eine Bildbiographie*, Berlin/Darmstadt/Wien: Deutsche Buchgemeinschaft, 1966.

Larson, Kelli A., *Hemingway. A Reference Guide, 1974–1989*, Basingstoke (Hamps.): Macmillan, 1990.

Lawrence, H. Lea, *A Hemingway Odyssey. Special Places in His Life*, Nashville (Tenn.): Cumberland House, 1999.

– *Prowling Papa's Waters. A Hemingway Odyssey*, Marietta (Ga.): Longstreet Press, 1992.

Lee, A. Robert (Hrsg.), *Ernest Hemingway. New Critical Essays*, Totowa, (N.J.): Barnes & Noble, 1983.

Leff, Leonard J., *Hemingway and His Conspirators. Hollywood, Scribners, and the Making of American Celebrity Culture*, Lanham (Md.): Rowman & Littlefield, 1997.

Lewis, Robert W., *Hemingway on Love*, Austin: University of Texas Press, 1965.

Lloyd R., Arnold, *High on the Wild with Hemingway*, Caidwell (Id.): Caxton Printers, 1968.

Lynn, Kenneth S., *Hemingway*, New York: Simon and Schuster, 1987.

Mandel, Miriam, *Reading Hemingway. The Facts and the Fictions*, Metuchen (N.J.): Scarecrow Press, 1995.

McCaffery, John K. M. (Hrsg.), *Ernest Hemingway. The Man and His Work*, New York: Cooper Square Publishers, 1950.

McDaniel, Melissa, *Ernest Hemingway*, Broomall (Pa.): Chelsea House, 1996.

McDowell, Nicholas, *Hemingway*, Hove (East Sussex): Wayland, 1988.

McIver, Stuart, *Hemingway's Key West*, Key West (Fla.): Pineapple Press, 1993.

Mellow, James R., *Hemingway. A Life Without Consequences*, Boston: Houghton Mifflin, 1992.

Messent, Peter, *Ernest Hemingway*, Basingstoke (Hamps.): Macmillan, 1992.

Meyers, Jeffrey (Hrsg.), *Hemingway. The Critical Heritage*, London/Boston/Henley: Routledge & Kegan Paul, 1982.

– *Hemingway. A Biography*, New York: Harper & Row, 1985.

Michener, James A., *Literary Reflections. Michener on Michener, Hemingway, Capote, and Others*, Austin (Tex.): State House Press, 1993.

Moddelmog, Debra, *Reading Desire. In Pursuit of Ernest Hemingway*, Ithaca (N.Y.): Cornell University Press, 1999.

Modern Fiction Studies. August 1955. H. 1. [Hemingway-Nummer.]

Möller Osmani, Kerstin, *In einem anderen Land. Ernest Hemingway und die »Junge Generation«. Möglichkeiten und Grenzen der Rezeption eines amerikanischen Autors in der frühen westdeutschen Nachkriegsliteratur*, Würzburg: Königshausen & Neumann, 1996 (Kieler Beiträge zur Anglistik und Amerikanistik, 13).

Montgomery, Constance Cappel, *Hemingway in Michigan*, New York: Fleet Publishing, 1966.

Moreland, Kim, *Medievalist Impulse in American Literature. Twain, Adams, Fitzgerald, and Hemingway*, Charlottesville: University Press of Virginia, 1996.

Nagel, James (Hrsg.), *Hemingway. The Writer in Context*, Boston: G. K. Hall, 1984.

– *Ernest Hemingway. The Oak Park Legacy*, Birmingham: University of Alabama Press, 1996.

Nahal, Chaman, *The Narrative Pattern in Ernest Hemingway's Fiction*, Madison (N. J.): Fairleigh Dickinson University Press, 1975.

Nelson, Gerald B. / Jones, Glory, *Hemingway. Life and Works*, New York: Facts on File, 1984.

Nelson, Raymond S., *Ernest Hemingway. Life, Work, and Criticism*, Fredericton (N.B.): York Press, 1984.

Nelson, Raymond S., *Hemingway. Expressionist Artist*, Chuckfield (West Sussex): Bell and Howell Information and Learning, 1986.

Nicolaisen, Peter, *Ernest Hemingway. Studien zum Bild der erzählten Welt*, Neumünster: Wachholtz, 1979 (Kieler Beiträge zur Anglistik und Amerikanistik, 12).

Oliver, Charles M., *Ernest Hemingway A to Z. The Essential Reference to His Life and Work*, New York: Checkmark Books, 1999.

Palin, Michael, *Michael Palin's Hemingway Adventure. Photographed and Designed by Basil Pao*, London: Weidenfeld & Nicolson, 1999.

Plath, James / Simons, Frank, *Remembering Ernest Hemingway*, Key West (Fla.): The Ketch & Yawl Press, 1999.

Raeburn, John, *Fame Became of Him. Hemingway as Public Writer*, Bloomington: Indiana University Press, 1984.

Reynolds, Michael, *Hemingway. An Annotated Chronology*, Detroit: Omnigraphics, 1991.

– *Hemingway. The 1930's*, Oxford: Blackwell, 1997.

– *Hemingway. The American Homecoming*, Oxford: Blackwell, 1992.

– *Hemingway. The Final Years*, Oxford: Blackwell, 1999.

– *Hemingway. The Paris Years*, Oxford: Blackwell, 1989.

– *Hemingway's First War. The Making of »A Farewell to Arms«*, Princeton (N.J.): Princeton University Press, 1976.

– *The Young Hemingway*, Oxford: Blackwell, 1986.

Rink, Paul, *Ernest Hemingway. Remaking Modern Fiction,* Chicago: Encyclopaedia Britannica Press, 1962.

Rosen, Kenneth H. (Hrsg.), *Hemingway Repossessed*, Westport/London: Greenwood Press, 1994.

Rovit, Earl, *Ernest Hemingway*, New York: Twayne, 1963.

Samuelson, Arnold, *With Hemingway. A Year in Key West and Cuba*, New York: Random House, 1984.

Sanderson, Stewart, *Ernest Hemingway*, New York: Grove Press, 1961.

Sarason, Bertram D., *Hemingway and the Sun Set*, Washington (D.C.): NCR Microcard Editions, 1972.

Scafella, Frank (Hrsg.), *Hemingway. Essays of Reassessment*, New York / Oxford: Oxford University Press, 1990.

Shaw, Samuel, *Hemingway*, New York: Ungar, 1972.

Singer, Kurt, *Hemingway. Life and Death of a Giant*, Los Angeles: Holloway House, 1961.

Smith, Paul (Hrsg.), *New Essays on Hemingway's Short Fiction*, Cambridge: Cambridge University Press, 1998.

– *A Reader's Guide to the Short Stories of Ernest Hemingway*, Boston: G. K. Hall, 1989.

Spilka, Mark, *Hemingway's Quarrel with Androgyny*, Omaha: University of Nebraska Press, 1995.

Stephens, Robert O., *Hemingway. The Critical Reception*, New York: B. Franklin, 1977.

– *Hemingway's Nonfiction. The Public Voice*, Chapel Hill: University of North Carolina Press, 1968.

Stresau: Hermann, *Ernest Hemingway*, Berlin: Wissenschaftsverlag Volker Spiess, 1985 (Köpfe des XX. Jahrhunderts, 6).

Svoboda, Frederic J. / Waldmeir, Joseph J. (Hrsg.), *Hemingway. Up in Michigan Perspectives*, East Lansing: Michigan State University Press, 1995.

Szumski, Bonnie (Hrsg.), »*The Old Man and the Sea*«, Westport/London: Greenwood Press, 1998.

Tessitore, John, *The Hunt and the Feast. A Life of Ernest Hemingway*, New York: Franklin Watts, 1996.

Unfried, Sarah P., *Man's Place in the Natural Order. A Study of Ernest Hemingway's Major Works*, New York: Gordon Press, 1976.

Villard, Henry Serano / Nagel, James (Hrsg.), *Hemingway in Love and War. The Lost Diary of Agnes von Kurowsky. Her Letters and Correspondence of Ernest Hemingway*, Chicago: Northwestern University Press, 1989.

Voss, Frederick S. / Reynolds, Michael S., *Picturing Hemingway. A Writer in His Time*, New Haven / London: Yale University Press, 1999.

Wagner, Linda W. (Hrsg.), *Ernest Hemingway. Six Decades of Criticism*, East Lansing: Michigan State University Press, 1987.

Wagner, Linda W. (Hrsg.), *Ernest Hemingway. A Reference Guide*, Boston: G. K. Hall, 1977.

– *Hemingway and Faulkner. Inventors/Masters*, Metuchen (N.J.): Scarecrow Press, 1975.

Wagner-Martin, Linda (Hrsg.), *A Historical Guide to Ernest Hemingway*, New York / Oxford: Oxford University Press, 2000.

Waldhorn, Arthur, *A Reader's Guide to Ernest Hemingway*, New York: Farrar, Straus & Giroux, 1972.

Watkins, Floyd C., *The Flesh and the Word. Eliot, Hemingway, Faulkner*, Nashville (Tenn.): Vanderbilt University Press, 1971.

Watts, Emily: *Ernest Hemingway and the Arts*, Urbana: University of Illinois Press, 1971.

Weber, Horst (Hrsg.), *Hemingway*, Darmstadt: Wissenschaftliche Buchgesellschaft, 1980 (Wege der Forschung, 546).

Weber, Ronald, *Hemingway's Art of Non-Fiction*, New York: Macmillan, 1990.

Weeks, Robert P. (Hrsg.), *Hemingway. A Collection of Critical Essays*, Englewood Cliffs (N.J.): Prentice-Hall, 1962.

Whiting, Charles, *Papa Goes to War. Ernest Hemingway in Europe (1944–45)*, Ramsbury: Crowood Press, 1990.

Whitlow, Roger, *Cassandra's Daughters. Women in Hemingway*, Westport/London: Greenwood Press, 1984 (Contributions in Women's Studies, 51).

Wilkinson, Myler, *Hemingway and Turgenev. The Nature of Literary Influence*, Ann Arbor (Mich.): University of Michigan Research Press, 1986 (Studies in Modern Literature, 59).

Williams, Wirt, *The Tragic Art of Hemingway*, Baton Rouge: Louisiana State University Press, 1981.

Wylder, Delbert E., *Hemingway's Heroes*, Albuquerque: University of New Mexico Press, 1969.

Young, Philip, *Ernest Hemingway*, New York: Holt, Rinehart and Winston, 1952. Neuausgabe u. d. T. *Ernest Hemingway. A Reconsideration*, University Park: Pennsylvania State University Press, 1966.

Zeittafel zu Leben und Werk
Ernest Hemingways

1899 Ernest Miller Hemingway am 21. Juli als zweites von sechs Kindern des Landarztes und Amateursportlers Clarence Edmonds Hemingway und seiner Frau, der Musiklehrerin Grace Hall Hemingway, in Oak Park, einem gutbürgerlichen Vorort von Chicago (Illinois) geboren. Jährliche Sommeraufenthalte an der Horton Bay, Lake Michigan, wo er mit dem Vater jagt und fischt.

1913 Besuch der Oak Park and River Forest Township High School. Auflehnung gegen Schule und Elternhaus (Hemingway reißt zweimal von zu Hause aus).

1916 Im Stil von Ring Lardner geschriebene Beiträge zur Schulzeitung *The Trapeze*.

1917 Statt eines Medizin- oder Musikstudiums (wie von den Eltern vorgesehen) Volontariat als Reporter beim *Kansas City Star* (bis April 1918).

1918 Ab Juni Dienst als Sanitätsfreiwilliger des Amerikanischen Roten Kreuzes in Oberitalien und Fronteinsatz in den Reihen der italienischen *arditi* (Infanterie). Am 8. Juli bei Fossalta di Piave schwer verwundet (227 Granatsplitterwunden, mehrere Maschinengewehreinschüsse, eine zerschmetterte Kniescheibe). Auszeichnung mit der Medaglia d'Argento al Valore Militare und dem Croce al Merito di Guerra. Genesung in einem Mailänder Krankenhaus. Liebesaffäre mit der Krankenschwester Agnes von Kurowsky (siehe den Film *Love and War*).

1919 Am 21. Januar Heimkehr als Kriegsinvalide nach Michigan. Hält Vorträge über sein Kriegserlebnis.

1920 Freier Mitarbeiter des *Toronto Star Weekly*.

1921 Am 3. September Heirat mit der Jugendfreundin Hadley Richardson in Chicago. Mitarbeit am *Cooperative Commonwealth*. Im November Überfahrt nach Frankreich, wo Hemingway als festbezahlter Sonderkorrespondent des *Toronto Daily Star* arbeitet – ein Amerikaner in Paris.

1922 Intensive journalistische Tätigkeit und ausgedehnte Reisen, etwa zur Berichterstattung über die Genfer Konferenz, den Griechisch-Türkischen Krieg und die Lausanner Konferenz. Daneben erste Kurzgeschichten und Gedichte. Bekanntschaft mit James Joyce und den amerikanischen Schriftstellern Gertrude Stein und Ezra Pound, die ihn zum Schreiben anhalten. Verlust eines bereits in Chicago begonnenen Romanmanuskripts in einem Eisenbahnabteil.

1923 Rückkehr nach Toronto. Am 10. Oktober Geburt des ersten Sohnes John Hadley Nicanor. Veröffentlichung von *Three Stories and Ten Poems*.

1924 Hemingway kündigt beim *Toronto Daily Star* und wird Paris-Korrespondent des *Hearst's Syndicated News Service*. Erster Spanienaufenthalt, erster Stierkampf. *in our time* (Kurzgeschichten).

1925 Im April Begegnung mit F. Scott Fitzgerald in Paris. Zweite Spanienreise. Im Juli Besuch der Fiesta de San Fermín in Pamplona.

1926 Durch Vermittlung F. Scott Fitzgeralds Begegnung mit Max Perkins, dem Verlagslektor von Scribner, der in Hemingway den Hauptsprecher der »verlorenen Generation« (Gertrude Stein) erkennt. *The Torrents of Spring* (Roman). *The Sun Also Rises* (Roman, auch u. d. T. *Fiesta*). Erste literarische Anerkennung.

1927 Im April lässt sich Hadley von Hemingway scheiden. Im Mai zweite Ehe mit der Modejournalistin Pauline Pfeiffer. *Men Without Women* (Kurzgeschichten).

1928 Auf Anregung von John Dos Passos Umzug von Paris nach Key West am äußersten Südzipfel Floridas. Arbeitsaufenthalte auf verschiedenen Ranches in Wyoming. Am 28. Juni Geburt des zweiten Sohnes Patrick. Im Dezember nimmt Hemingways Vater sich das Leben.

1929 Längerer Spanienaufenthalt. *A Farewell to Arms* (Roman).

1930 In Key West und auf der L-Bar-T Ranch in Wyoming Arbeit an dem Stierkampfbuch *Death in the Afternoon*.

1931 Kauf eines Hauses in Key West. Geburt des dritten Sohnes Gregory.

1932 *Death in the Afternoon*.

1933 »Letters« für das Magazin *Esquire. Winner Take Nothing* (Kurzgeschichten).

1934 Viermonatige Safari in Afrika.

1935 *Green Hills of Africa* (Reiseschilderungen).

1936 Aufenthalte in Wyoming und auf Kuba. Sammelt Geld zum Kauf von Krankenwagen für die republikanische Seite im Spanischen Bürgerkrieg. Im Dezember Bekanntschaft mit der Schriftstellerin Martha Gellhorn.

1937 Im Februar als Kriegsberichterstatter für die *North American Newspaper Alliance* nach Spanien. Beginn der Liebesaffäre mit Martha Gellhorn. Drehbuch für den republikanischen Film *Spanish Earth* (Regie: Joris Ivens). *To Have and Have Not* (Roman).

1938 *The Fifth Column and The First Forty-nine Stories* (Theaterstück über den Spanischen Bürgerkrieg und Kurzgeschichten).

1939 Trennung von Pauline. Lebt mit Martha auf dem 15 Morgen großen Landgut Finca Vigía in San Francisco de Paula, einem Vorort von Havanna. Schreibt in Paris, Havanna, Key West, Wyoming und Sun Valley (Idaho) an dem Bürgerkriegsroman *For Whom the Bell Tolls*.

1940 Im November lässt sich Pauline Pfeiffer von Hemingway scheiden. Dritte Ehe mit Martha Gellhorn. Kauf des Landguts. *For Whom the Bell Tolls*.

1941 Mit Martha als Kriegsberichterstatter des Magazins *PM* nach China.

1942 Rüstet seine Barkasse *Pilar* für Patrouillenfahrten gegen deutsche U-Boote in der Karibik aus.

1943 Martha vollendet ihren Roman *Liana* und wird Kriegsberichterstatterin für *Collier's*, während Hemingway zwischen 1940 und 1946 nichts Nennenswertes produziert. Spannungen in der Ehe.

1944 Hemingway löst Martha als Kriegsberichterstatter für *Collier's* ab. Fliegt bei Einsätzen der Royal Air Force mit. Schwere Verletzungen bei einem Verkehrsunfall. Im Mai Begegnung mit der *Time*-Korrespondentin Mary Welsh Monks. Am 6. Juni nimmt »Papa« Hemingway an der Landung der alliierten Truppen in der Normandie, später an der Befreiung von Paris teil (mit einem kleinen Trupp Soldaten »befreit« er das »Ritz«). Ein amerikanisches Kriegsgericht spricht Hemingway von der Anklage frei, seinen Status als Nonkombattant verletzt zu haben.

1945 Verleihung des Bronze Star. Rückkehr nach New York und Kuba, wohin Mary ihm folgt. Im September Scheidung von Martha Gellhorn.

1946 Am 21. März vierte Ehe mit Mary Welsh Monks in Havanna. Hemingway arbeitet an einer »Trilogie«. Erste Anzeichen von Hypertonie, Depression und Paranoia.

1948–49 Mehrmonatiger Italienaufenthalt mit Mary. In Venedig Liebesaffäre mit der achtzehnjährigen Adriana Ivancich.

1949–50 Mehrmonatiger Frankreich- und Italienaufenthalt.

1950 Besuch Adriana Ivancichs auf Finca Vigía. Der Roman *Across the River and Into the Trees* wird von der Kritik abgelehnt.

1951 Hemingway beendet den Roman *Islands in the Stream* (veröffentlicht 1970). Im Juni stirbt seine Mutter, im Oktober seine ehemalige Frau Pauline.

1952 Das Magazin *Life* veröffentlicht die Novelle *The Old Man and the Sea* zunächst in Fortsetzungen, sodann – mit einer Auflage von 5 Millionen Exemplaren – in ihrer Gesamtheit.

1953 Buchverfilmung. Am 4. Mai Verleihung des Pulitzer-Preises für *The Old Man and the Sea*. Award of Merit der American Academy of Arts and Letters. Ab September halten sich die Hemingways in Kenia zu einer Safari auf.

1954   Am 23. Januar macht Hemingways Flugzeug im Dschungel Ugandas eine Bruchlandung. Das Ersatzflugzeug stürzt ebenfalls ab und geht in Flammen auf. Die Zeitungen bringen verfrühte Nachrufe. In Venedig erholt sich Hemingway von seinen schweren Verletzungen. Im Juni Rückkehr nach Kuba. Am 28. Oktober Zuerkennung des Literaturnobelpreises, ausdrücklich für *The Old Man and the Sea*. Hemingway kann die Auszeichnung aufgrund seiner angeschlagenen Gesundheit nicht persönlich entgegennehmen.

1955   Beginn der Arbeit an dem Afrikajournal *True at First Light* (veröffentlicht 1999).

1956   Im Pariser »Ritz« aufgefundene Tagebücher bilden die Grundlage für die Erinnerungen *A Moveable Feast* (veröffentlicht 1964).

1959   Beunruhigt über die kubanische Revolution, kauft sich Hemingway ein Haus in Ketchum (Idaho). Letzte Spanienreise. Schreibt einen ausgedehnten Artikel über zwei spanische Stierkämpfer, veröffentlicht als *The Dangerous Summer* (1964). Feiert seinen 60. Geburtstag in Málaga.

1960   Im Juli verlässt Hemingway Kuba. Er leidet an Depressionen und Stimmungsumschwüngen. Im November Einweisung in die Mayo Clinic Rochester (Minnesota), wo er einer Elektroschocktherapie unterzogen wird.

1961   Ende Januar Entlassung. Nach zwei Selbstmordversuchen im April erneute Einweisung in die Klinik. Am 26. Juni als geheilt entlassen. Am 2. Juli Selbstmord durch zwei Schüsse in den Mund. Begräbnis auf dem Friedhof von Ketchum.

Nachwort

Als Ernest Hemingway, knapp zweiundsechzig Jahre alt, am Sonntag, dem 2. Juli 1961 um sieben Uhr in der Frühe seinem Dasein mit zwei Schüssen aus einer doppelläufigen Schrotflinte ein freiwilliges Ende setzte, gab er jenen mythischen Kampf auf, zu dem er, unter gewaltigen Anstrengungen, sein ganzes Leben stilisiert hatte und von dem in immer neuen Anläufen und Varianten sein erzählerisches Werk handelt. Der amerikanische Großschriftsteller, der nach den Traumata früher physischer und psychischer Versehrungen auf den Schlachtfeldern des Krieges und der Liebe unablässig dem Kult des Virilen und Heroischen gehuldigt hatte, für den das Abenteuer der menschlichen Existenz in erster Linie aus Großwildjagd und Stierkampf, Angelsport und Preisboxen, Skifahren und Schwimmen, exzessivem Trinken und anderen Beweisen männlicher Tatkraft bestand, gab sich geschlagen, als Körper und Geist ihm den Dienst versagten. Schwere Depressionen über seinen zerrütteten Gesundheitszustand, über drohenden Gedächtnisverlust und künstlerisches Unvermögen resultierten in mehreren Selbstmordversuchen, die endlich zum gewünschten Ziel führten – ein Beleg für Schopenhauers These, »daß, sobald es dahin gekommen ist, daß die Schrecknisse des Lebens die Schrecknisse des Todes überwiegen, der Mensch seinem Leben ein Ende macht«.[1] In der Entscheidung für den Freitod wie in der Wahl der Todesart folgte Hemingway dem Beispiel seines Vaters.

---

1 Arthur Schopenhauer, *Werke*, nach den Ausgaben letzter Hand hrsg. von Ludger Lütkehaus, Bd. 5: *Parerga und Paralipomena: Kleine philosophische Schriften*, Bd. 2, Zürich: Haffmanns, 1988, S. 276.

Dabei hatte er noch ein Jahrzehnt zuvor mit seinem Meisterstück *The Old Man and the Sea* dem alternden Menschen und seinem unbezähmbaren Lebens- und Überlebenswillen ein literarisches Denkmal gesetzt, wie es zärtlicher und liebevoller kaum hätte ausfallen können. Zentrale Motive und Themen, die Hemingways Œuvre auszeichnen, finden sich gebündelt und geläutert in diesem kompakten und doch komplexen Werk, einem Text, mit dem sich Hemingway nach dem Misserfolg seines venezianischen Liebesromans *Across the River and Into the Trees* (1950) wieder in die Gunst des Publikums und der Kritik einzuschreiben vermochte. Die menschlich anrührende Geschichte von dem alten kubanischen Fischer, der nach vierundachtzig Tagen glückloser Ausfahrt unverdrossen erneut aufs offene Meer hinausrudert, den Kampf mit einem mächtigen Marlin sucht und besteht, nur um am Ende mit leeren Händen nach Hause zurückzukehren, zieht das Resümee einer stoischen Lebensauffassung, deren oberstes Gebot lautet, der Mühsal des Lebens und der Unausweichlichkeit des Todes gleichermaßen gefasst ins Auge zu sehen. Auszug und Heimkehr, Hoffnung und Enttäuschung, Phantasie und Wirklichkeit, Triumph und Tragik, Sieg und Niederlage, Anspruch und Gelingen, Gewinn und Verlust, Tun und Leiden (»But I will show him what a man can do and what a man endures«) sind integrale Bestandteile ein und desselben unabänderlichen Lebensrhythmus.

Mit der Arbeit an dieser Erzählung – Kritik und Forschung sind sich nicht einig, ob es sich um einen Kurzroman, eine Novelle oder eine längere Short Story handelt – begann Hemingway im Dezember 1951, angeregt von einer wahren Begebenheit. Ein Beweggrund für die Abfassung der Geschichte dürfte seine zunehmende Vereinsamung, seine Furcht vor dem Alter und das Gefühl der Todesnähe gewesen sein. Zwei Menschen, die ihm besonders nahe gestanden hatten, waren in rascher Folge gestorben: im Juni 1951 seine Mutter Grace Hall Hemingway, im Oktober 1951 seine zweite Frau Pauline. Im Februar 1952, kurz vor Vollendung der ersten Textfassung, erlag sein Verleger, Mentor und Vaterersatz Charles Scribner einem Herzinfarkt.

Der verarbeitete Stoff weist nicht nur Bezüge zu literarischen Vorläufern wie der phantastischen Ballade *The Rime of the Ancyent Marinere* (1798) von Samuel Taylor Coleridge, dem Walfangroman *Moby Dick* (1851) von Herman Melville und Stephen Cranes Erzählung *The Open Boat* (1897) auf, sondern geht auf einen eigenen Artikel aus dem Jahre 1936 zurück; den in »On the Blue Water (A Gulf Stream Letter)« geschilderten Vorfall hatte Hemingway schon 1939 beträchtlich erweitern wollen.

Rein oberflächlich, auf der Handlungsebene betrachtet, schildert Hemingway mit eindrucksvoller, nahezu fotografischer Realistik eine überschaubare Episode aus dem Arbeitsalltag des armen, seit dem Tod seiner Frau vereinsamten kubanischen Fischers Santiago, der, wie schon einmal in seinem Leben, seit fast drei Monaten keinen Fang mehr getan hat, die Hoffnung auf reiche Beute jedoch nicht fahren lässt; mag auch das Segel seines kleinen, vom Pech verfolgten Bootes aussehen wie »the flag of permanent defeat«, seine meerblauen Augen sind »undefeated«. Zuversicht und furchtlose Entschlossenheit noch im hohen Alter sind hervorstechende Charaktermerkmale dieses geborenen Fischers (»You were born to be a fisherman as the fish was born to be a fish«), für den der Fischfang mehr ist als nur ein Brotberuf, nämlich eine eingefleischte Lebensweise.

In prägnanten Details werden die Vorkehrungen und Zurüstungen des Fischzugs beschrieben, für den Santiago diesmal weiter hinausfährt denn je zuvor. Begleitet von Fischen und Vögeln, mit denen er ebenso Zwiesprache hält wie mit den eigenen Händen, verbringt er volle drei Tage und Nächte in küstenfernen Gewässern des Golfs von Mexiko und erlebt nach langer, oft monotoner Warterei und wiederholten Bittgebeten das Glück, dass ein gewaltiger, das eigene Boot an Länge überragender Marlin anbeißt. In einem tagelangen Zweikampf von nachgerade epischen Ausmaßen gelingt es Santiago mit Mut, Geschicklichkeit und Ausdauer, den Fisch zu besiegen, einzubringen und zu vertäuen. Doch nun erst beginnt die eigentliche Auseinandersetzung: das Ringen mit Mitbewerbern aus dem Reich der Natur, den räuberischen Mako- und Schaufelhaien, die seine Beute so beharrlich anfallen, dass von dem prachtvollen, noblen Geschöpf nur noch ein abgefressenes Skelett übrig bleibt. Körperlich erschöpft, doch geistig ungebrochen läuft Santiago seinen Heimathafen (Cojímar) an und plant bereits die nächste Ausfahrt; nur eine kaum merkliche Veränderung in seinem Körper lässt auf den bevorstehenden Tod schließen: »In the night I spat something strange and felt something in my chest was broken« (S. 104).

Der kopulative Titel *The Old Man and the Sea* (wohl eine Eingebung des mit Hemingway befreundeten kubanischen Fischers Gregorio Fuentes) bindet Mann und Meer, Mensch und Natur schicksalhaft aneinander. Der Fischer ist darauf angewiesen, jenem bald freundlichen, bald feindlichen Element, das die Nahrungsmittel, die es birgt, ebenso oft verweigert, wie es sie gewährt (»a fishless desert«), seinen Lebensunterhalt abzutrotzen; er tötet, um zu leben: »I did it to keep me alive and feed many people« (S. 88). Ebenso aneinander gekettet (»I'am being towed by a fish and I'am the towing bitt«) sind Jäger und Gejagter, das Raubtier Mensch und sein Beutetier, der Marlin oder Speerfisch, beide mit ähnlichen Tötungswerkzeugen bewaffnet.

Hemingways künstlerische Leistung besteht darin, in diese einfach konstruierte, schlicht erzählte Handlung mehrere Bedeutungsschichten eingearbeitet zu haben, die genauerer Auslotung bedürfen. Die Anglergeschichte vom »sportlichen« Wettkampf zwischen Mensch und Tier weist eine spirituelle oder metaphysische Dimension auf, die die bloße Materialität des Erzählten übersteigt.

Da ist zunächst einmal die alle Alters- und Generationenunterschiede überbrückende Freundschaft zwischen dem Außenseiter Santiago und dem jungen Manolin, eine für Hemingway typische Männerfreundschaft, hinter deren spröder Wortkargheit sich von tiefem Vertrauen geprägte fürsorgliche Zuneigung verbirgt. Manolin, der den Fischer vierzig Tage lang aufs Meer hinaus begleitet hatte, ehe seine Eltern ihn zu sich zurückbeorderten, versorgt den einsamen Alten mit Mahlzeiten und Fischködern, leistet ihm Gesellschaft, geht ihm zur Hand und pflegt seine Wunden. Am Anfang und am Ende der Erzählung werden die beiden in ihrer dreifachen Beziehung als Vater und Sohn, Lehrer und Schüler (»The old man had taught the boy to fish and the boy loved him«) sowie Meister und Jünger (»I would like to serve in some way«) vorgestellt. Während seines elementaren Kampfes mit dem großen Fisch wünscht Santiago sich nichts sehnlicher als die Gegenwart des Jüngeren, sei es als Bootsmaat, der ihm hilft, den Fisch zu bezwingen, sei es als Gesprächspartner, der ihn der Notwendigkeit des Selbstgesprächs enthebt.

Doch damit erschöpft sich die ungewöhnlich loyale Beziehung zwischen den Repräsentanten des Alters und der Jugend (und damit des Lebenszyklus) nicht. In Wahrheit ist die mantraähnliche Anrufung des Knaben im Boot Santiagos Versuch, sich im Medium der Imagination und der Erinnerung der eigenen Jugend zu versichern und deren Willenskraft und Mut heraufzubeschwören. Die gleiche psychologische Funktion hat der mehrfach wiederkehrende Traum von den friedlich am afrikanischen Strand spielenden jungen Löwen, denen er als Jugendlicher zugeschaut hatte: »He no longer dreamed of storms, nor of women, nor of great occurrences, nor of great fish, nor fights, nor contests of strength, nor of his wife. He only dreamed of places now and of the lions on the beach. They played like young cats in the dusk and he loved them as he loved the boy« (S. 17 f.).

Magische Formel einerseits, allegorisches Traumbild andererseits sind die Quellen, aus denen sich Santiagos unbeugsamer Kampfgeist speist. Wie er seinen Körper mit dem rohen Fleisch und Blut des Thunfischs, der Goldmakrele und der fliegenden Fische nährt, so seine Seele mit den Bildern einer unbeschwerteren, kampflosen Existenz. Doch der Traum drückt nicht den Wunsch nach Rückkehr in einen pastoralen, paradiesischen Urzustand der Unschuld und der Untätigkeit aus, sondern dient ihm als Springquell der Stärkung und des Glücksempfindens in einer Zeit körperlicher

Angegriffenheit. Dass er im Schlusssatz der Erzählung erneut von den anmutigen Löwenjungen träumt, verleiht dem Buch die letztendlich optimistische Note.

Auch das Ethos und Pathos eines heroischen Kampfes auf Leben und Tod (»I'll stay with you until I am dead«) hat einen tieferen symbolischen Gehalt. *The Old Man and the Sea* lässt sich lesen als »Parabel über die Situation des Menschen, der als Hoffender ausfährt und kämpft, als Geschlagener zurückkehrt und doch wieder aufbricht«.[2] Die Dialektik von objektiver Sinnlosigkeit und subjektivem Sinnbedürfnis, die in der Ausbildung eines moralischen Verhaltenskodex des »Trotz alledem« resultiert, erinnert an Albert Camus' existentialistische Deutung des antiken Mythos von Sisyphos, welche programmatisch der Absurdität des Daseins ein Optimum an Lebensintensität entgegensetzt. Die der Ausfahrt des Fischers vergleichbare Lebensreise des Menschen als *homo viator* hat sich an jener Maxime zu orientieren, die im Zentrum des Buches steht: »But man is not made for defeat. [...] A man can be destroyed but not defeated« (S. 86).

Der Gedanke der im Kampf gewonnenen Identität und Dignität wird durch die häufigen Verweise auf das Baseballspiel eines DiMaggio und die Erinnerung an das Kräftemessen mit dem schwarzen Dockarbeiter aus Cienfuegos, das Santiago den Beinamen »El Campeón« eintrug, noch verstärkt. Dass Santiago seinen Fang nicht unversehrt einbringt – weder er noch sein Fisch kommen unbeschädigt davon –, bezeugt das Existential, dass jedes Fortschreiten, jeder Erfolg, jeder Triumph seinen Preis hat, den es zu bezahlen gilt:

2 Rudolf Haas, »*Der alte Mann und das Meer*«, in: Gero von Wilpert (Hrsg.), *Lexikon der Weltliteratur*, Bd. 3, München: dtv, 1977, S. 40.

»Fishing kills me exactly as it keeps me alive« (S. 88). Nietzsches »Leben ist Kampf und Spiel« und Schopenhauers »Leben ist Leiden« (»›How much did you suffer?‹ ›Plenty,‹ the old man said«) werden in Santiagos Geschichte kurzgeschlossen.

Doch der einseitigen Idee vom Überlebenskampf als Kampf des Menschen gegen die Natur steht Santiagos Verlangen nach Verbrüderung mit den Geschöpfen der Natur entgegen. Im Laufe der Geschichte spricht er die Tiere der Luft und des Wassers, von der Grasmücke über die Tümmler bis zu den fliegenden Fischen, wieder und wieder als seine Freunde und Brüder an. Der Ehrenplatz in dieser Galerie der Mitgeschöpfe gebührt dem Marlin: »Never have I seen a greater, or more beautiful, or a calmer or more noble thing than you, brother« (S. 76 f.). In einem überschwänglichen Ausbruch kosmischen Einsseins von Mensch und Natur bezieht Santiago sogar die Sterne am Firmament in diese Gleichung mit ein. Den »Wunschtraum der Jahrtausende«, »grenzenlos Natur zu beherrschen, den Kosmos in ein unendliches Jagdgebiet zu verwandeln«,[3] konterkariert er mit der trockenen Feststellung: »But it is good that we do not have to try to kill the sun or the moon or the stars. It is enough to live on the sea and kill our true brothers« (S. 63).

Die fast aussichtslose Härte des Duells, die Ebenbürtigkeit des Gegners, der ebenso gut Sieger wie Beute sein könnte, veranlasst den Fischer zu einer hochreflektierten Philosophie der Brüderlichkeit aller Krea-

3 Max Horkheimer / Theodor W. Adorno, *Dialektik der Aufklärung. Philosophische Fragmente*, Amsterdam: Querido, 1947, S. 298. Den Hinweis auf dieses und das folgende Zitat verdanke ich Karsten Fischer, »Ein Geruch von Grausamkeit. Nietzsche als Avantgardist der Rationalisierungskritik«, in: *Neue Rundschau* 111 (2000), H. 1, S. 58–76.

tur und damit zu einer Widerrufung jenes anthropozentrischen Kalküls, welches Kant in einem an die Genesis angelehnten Essay nach freier Wahl der Lebensweise, nach Sittsamkeit und Erwartung des Künftigen als vierte Folge des Gebrauchs der Vernunft behandelt, nämlich den Anspruch des Menschen, Zweck der Natur zu sein, gegen den kein anderes Lebewesen einen »Mitbewerber« abgeben kann: »Das erstemal, daß er zum Schafe sagte: *den Pelz, den du trägst, hat dir die Natur nicht für dich, sondern für mich gegeben*, ihm ihn abzog, und sich selbst anlegte, ward er eines Vorrechtes inne, welches er, vermöge seiner Natur, über alle Tiere hatte, die er nun nicht mehr als seine Mitgenossen an der Schöpfung, sondern als seinem Willen überlassene Mittel und Werkzeuge zu Erreichung seiner beliebigen Absichten ansah.«[4]

In Santiagos Augen ist der Platz des Menschen in der natürlichen Ordnung ein anderer. Gerade die Mühseligkeit seines Lebens überzeugt den Fischer davon, dass die »*Entlassung* [des Menschen] aus dem Mutterschoße der Natur«,[5] das vollkommene Abstreifen der Tierverwandtschaft, eine Fehlentwicklung sei. Fischer und Fisch führen einen verbissenen, hin- und herwogenden Zweikampf, in dessen Verlauf der Mensch dem Tier auf eine Weise näher rückt, die ein »heiliges Band«[6] von der nämlichen Art stiftet, wie

4 Immanuel Kant, »Mutmaßlicher Anfang der Menschengeschichte«, in: I. K., *Werke*, hrsg. von Wilhelm Weischedel, Bd. 11: *Schriften zur Anthropologie, Geschichtsphilosophie, Politik und Pädagogik 1*, Frankfurt a. M.: Suhrkamp,⁴1982 (¹1977), S. 91.
5 Ebd.
6 Sigmund Freud, »Totem und Tabu«, in: S. F., *Studienausgabe*, hrsg. von Alexander Mitscherlich, Angela Richards und James Strachey †, Bd. 9: *Fragen der Gesellschaft, Ursprünge der Religion*, Frankfurt a. M.: Fischer, 1982, S. 422.

Freud es in seiner Abhandlung *Totem und Tabu* für die festliche Totemmahlzeit rekonstruiert hat, welche Clan, Opfertier und göttliches Totemtier miteinander vereint.

Santiagos beschwörender Umgang mit dem großen Fisch erinnert an die frühe totemistische Periode der Menschheitsgeschichte, als die Tötung von Tieren ein nur ausnahmsweise gestatteter Akt war, für den Abbitte geleistet werden musste: »Alle [Opfer-]Tiere sind ursprünglich heilig, ihr Fleisch ist verboten und darf nur bei feierlicher Gelegenheit unter Teilnahme des ganzen Stammes genossen werden. Das Schlachten des Tieres kommt dem Vergießen von Stammesblut gleich [...].«[7] Die Jagd auf Tiere, zu der auch der Fischfang zählt, ist ursprünglicher als die Zähmung, Haltung und Züchtung von Tieren. Geleitet von seiner hohen Achtung vor dem Tierreich, stellt Santiago auch hierüber Überlegungen an. In Auflehnung gegen den biblischen Unterwerfungsgestus herzloser Naturbeherrschung und Naturvergewaltigung kann er sich des Gedankens nicht erwehren, eine Sünde begangen, jenes archaische Tötungsverbot übertreten zu haben, für das der Mensch, will er sich als des Tieres würdig erweisen, im Zeremoniell des Opferritus Verzeihung erbitten musste. So heißt es über den früheren Fang eines Marlins: »[...] we begged her pardon and butchered her promptly« (S. 40). Gegenüber der gedankenlosen Routine der Massenschlachtung führt Hemingways Fischer Tötung und Verzehr als bewusstes Ritual vor: »Hemingway in *The Old Man and the Sea* comes close to unqualified celebration of primitive or childlike inti-

---

7 Ebd., S. 421.

macy with nature as the means to spiritual transcendence.«[8]

Der Mensch ist dem Tier lediglich dank »treachery« und »trickery« überlegen (»Man is not much beside the great birds and beasts«) und nicht etwa aufgrund des monotheistisch abgesicherten Macht- und Unterdrückungsanspruchs der jüdisch-christlichen Schöpfungsgeschichte; »Und Gott segnete sie und sprach zu ihnen: Seid fruchtbar und mehret euch und füllet die Erde und machet sie euch untertan und *herrschet über die Fische im Meer* und über die Vögel unter dem Himmel und über das Vieh und über alles Getier, das auf Erden kriecht« (1. Mose 1,26,28; Hervorhebung vom Hrsg.). Die in die Erzählung eingestreuten Jagdbilder von Fregattvogel und fliegendem Fisch, Falke und Grasmücke, Schildkröte und Portugiesischer Galeere, Hai und Marlin unterstreichen die Tierähnlichkeit des Menschen als einem der Glieder in einer universalen Nahrungskette (»[...] everything kills everything else in some way«). Jedoch nur aus dem Mitleid (»pity« und »sorrow«) mit dem zu tötenden und endlich mit dem getöteten Tier, nur aus der Demut dem Tier gegenüber kann Stolz erwachsen.

Schon seine mechanisch dahingemurmelten Gebete verraten, dass Santiago kein religiöser Mensch im Sinne des christlichen Gottesglaubens ist; die Heiligenbilder an den Wänden seiner Hütte sind eine Hinterlassenschaft seiner Frau. Auch die Assoziationen mit den Wundmalen Jesu und andere christologische Anspielungen sind dem Gehalt der Erzählung äußerlich. Doch

8 Katharine T. Jobes, »Introduction«, in: K. T. J. (Hrsg.), *Twentieth Century Interpretations of »The Old Man and the Sea«. A Collection of Critical Essays*, Englewood Cliffs (N.J.): Prentice-Hall, 1968, S. 15.

Santiagos geistige Auseinandersetzung mit Tod und Tötung verraten echte religiöse Skrupel, die der Einfühlung in sein Totemtier, den Marlin, geschuldet sind.

Ein weiterer Bedeutungskern, der sich aus dem Handlungsgeflecht der Erzählung herausschälen lässt, ist selbstreferentieller Natur. Danach wäre die Geschichte des Fischers als Gleichnis für die Entwicklung des vereinsamten Schriftstellers zu lesen, der im Jahre 1951 am Ende seiner körperlichen, geistigen und schöpferischen Kräfte angelangt zu sein schien. Hat Santiago vierundachtzig Tage lang keinen Fisch anlanden können, so hatte Hemingway elf Jahre lang kein nennenswertes literarisches Werk hervorgebracht. Seit *For Whom the Bell Tolls* (1940) hatte er lediglich einen Roman veröffentlicht, der von der Kritik einstimmig als banale und vulgäre Selbstparodie abgelehnt worden war. Demnach symbolisiert *The Old Man and the Sea* auch den Kampf des Künstlers um die Beherrschung seines ästhetischen Materials; nicht von ungefähr wird die Angelleine an einer Stelle mit einem dicken Bleistift verglichen. In seiner Rede zur Annahme des Nobelpreises für Literatur spielte Hemingway auf ebendiese »Ausfahrt« des Schriftstellers an: »How simple the writing of literature would be if it were only necessary to write in another way what has been well written. It is because we have had such great writers in the past that *a writer is driven far out past where he can go, out to where no one can help him*«[9] (Hervorhebung vom Hrsg.).

The Old Man and the Sea, wohl sein bekanntestes und meistgelesenes Werk, ist auch ein Selbstzeugnis

9 Zit. nach: K. T. Jobes, S. 9.

Hemingwayscher Revitalisierung; es handelt nicht nur von der Einsamkeit des Alters (»No one should be alone in their old age, he thought. But it is unavoidable«), sondern auch von der Einsamkeit des Künstlers, der, wenn er seiner künstlerischen Mission genügen soll, kühn an die äußersten Grenzen seiner schöpferischen Potenz vordringen muss. Das Ringen um Form und Stil, das Streben nach kraftvollem sprachlichem Ausdruck, künstlerischer Wahrheit und persönlicher Authentizität wird hier in Parallele zu dem Bemühen des Fischers um vollendete Beherrschung seines Handwerks gesehen. Doch ebenso wie der Fischer außer »precision« auch »luck« benötigt, ist der Schriftsteller auf Inspiration angewiesen.

Hemingway kam zu dem Schluss, dass der lakonisch verknappte, aber symbolisch angereicherte, hintergründige Prosastil der Erzählung die Ausbeute eines solchen Wagnisses war: »It's as though I had gotten finally what I had been waiting for all my life.«[10] Die Schwedische Akademie ist ihm in dieser Einschätzung gefolgt; im Oktober 1954 erkannte ihm das Nobelpreiskomitee die höchste internationale literarische Auszeichnung zu – »for his mastery of the art of narrative, most recently demonstrated in *The Old Man and the Sea*, and for the influence that he has exerted on contemporary style«.[11]

Hans-Christian Oeser

10 Zit. nach: Angel Capellán, *Hemingway and the Hispanic World*, Ann Arbor (Mich.): University of Michigan Research Press, 1985, S. 112.
11 Zit. nach: Peter Wilhelm, *The Nobel Prize*, London: Springwood Books, 1983, S. 104.

Inhalt

Fremdsprachentexte

IN RECLAMS UNIVERSAL-BIBLIOTHEK

Amerikanische Literatur (Auswahl)

Ernest Hemingway: The Old Man and the Sea. 140 S. UB 9075 – The Snows of Kilimanjaro. Six Stories. 176 S. UB 9120

Patricia Highsmith: A Shot from Nowhere. Six Stories. 160 S. UB 9262 – The Talented Mr. Ripley. 437 S. UB 9145

Denis Johnson: Jesus' Son. 157 S. UB 9092

Kressmann Taylor: Address Unknown. 63 S. UB 9107

Cormac McCarthy: The Road. 296 S. UB 19757

Nick McDonell: Twelve. 237 S. UB 9127

Herman Melville: Bartleby. 88 S. UB 9190

Arthur Miller: Death of a Salesman. 171 S. UB 9172 – The Crucible. 224 S. UB 9257

Mexican-American Short Stories. 179 S. UB 9124

Modern American Short Stories. 160 S. UB 9216

New York Fiction. 154 S. UB 9070

Eugene O'Neill: Long Day's Journey into Night. 216 S. UB 9252

Edgar Allan Poe: The Gold-Bug and Other Tales. 192 S. UB 9173 – The Murders in the Rue Morgue. 80 S. UB 9088

Morton Rhue: Give a Boy a Gun. 195 S. UB 9111

Philip Roth: Everyman. 207 S. UB 19751

John Steinbeck: Of Mice and Men. 173 S. UB 9253 – Tortilla Flat. 280 S. UB 9027

James Thurber: Stories and Fables of Our Time. Ill. 88 S. UB 9232

West Side Story. A Musical. (Jerome Robbins / Arthur Laurents / Leonard Bernstein / Stephen Sondheim.) 136 S. UB 9212

Thornton Wilder: The Bridge of San Luis Rey. 152 S. UB 9195 – Our Town. 127 S. UB 9168

Tennessee Williams: Cat on a Hot Tin Roof. 223 S. UB 9039 – The Glass Menagerie. 149 S. UB 9178 – A Streetcar Named Desire. 199 S. UB 9240

Philipp Reclam jun. Stuttgart